Life is not measured by the number of breaths you take, but by the moments that take your breath away.

D1484672

Let us
take your
breath away

$\mathcal{I}$t is with great pleasure that we bring you our exciting new plan book pictorial. The homes featured in this book illustrate the log home lifestyle and what it means to our True North log home owner.

Whether it's a rustic retreat or a distinctive family home, we know that you have a passion for the ambience and lifestyle that can only be created with a log home. We also know you are looking for the peace of mind that comes from owning a log home that truly meets the ultimate standard in technology and craftsmanship.

ENJOYING PRECIOUS MOMENTS

We chose the saying, *"Life is not measured by the number of breaths you take, but by the moments that take your breath away,"* to stimulate our customers' imaginations and express the essence of True North Log Homes. Our lives are about snippets or moments in time: from happy fun filled moments and magical family moments to exciting and loving moments, these are the times that give us true pleasure in life. Log homes naturally create an environment that allows these precious moments to be shared. Living in a log home invokes a sense of calmness, peace and solitude that helps us escape – if only for a few moments – from the hectic pace of our day-to-day lives.

For over 20 years we have celebrated the log home lifestyle. While being true to our roots, we have developed the most technologically-advanced log home on the planet. We take great pride in the innovative spirit of our family, which is reflected in our 18 (soon to be 24) Canadian and U.S. patents exclusive to True North Log Homes. The True North technology is comprised of many minute details and it is our attention to these details that create the peace of mind that we provide to our customers.

The following pages demonstrate True North's commitment to bringing these precious moments to each of our customers. We hope you enjoy our new log home plan book and that you find a dream home that truly takes your breath away!

Robert A. Wrightman, C.E.O.

Contents

Moments in *Time*

The True North Story

Canada

United States of America

Great Britain

Ireland

Germany

Mexico

South Korea

Bahamas

Japan

A FAMILY BUSINESS FOUNDED ON TECHNOLOGY, STEEPED IN PRIDE

True North Log Homes is the manufacturer of the best-engineered log homes in North America – homes of exceptional quality, beauty and durability. Located in Bracebridge, Ontario, deep in the heart of the ruggedly beautiful Muskoka region, True North Log Homes is a 100 percent Canadian company. The True North Log Homes story is one of technical innovation, hard work, and a steadfast commitment to being the undisputed leader in the construction of high quality log homes.

A FAMILY WITH DEDICATION AND INNOVATIVE SPIRIT

Ron Wrightman made his start in the log home industry in 1979, founding his first successful log home company, which is still in operation today. Ron's son, Rob, managed the original plant while acquiring his carpenter's papers. After the sale of the initial company, Rob worked with the new owners, teaching them how to operate the plant, and then spent the following year building homes on their behalf. Rob then moved on to attain his real estate license and after a highly successful five years of selling cottage properties, approached his father Ron with a plan to re-enter the log home industry.

In 1986 the father and son team co-founded True North Log Homes. After ten years, Rob assumed control of the company when his father retired. Rob continues the family innovative spirt by recently acquiring 4 of his own (soon to be 10) new patents, complimenting Ron's original 14 patents.

INNOVATIVE TECHNOLOGY

At the heart of True North technology is the patented Keylock Air Seal Corner®, which has revolutionized log home construction. This joinery system is what distinguishes a True North log home from every other. The absence of nails, screws or lag bolts in the True North joinery system is the trademark of this superior construction method. True North is the only log home company willing to offer a 25-year warranty against air infiltration – a testimony to the confidence that the Wrightmans have in their log home system.

WORLD CLASS RECOGNITION

Through an untiring dedication to excellence, along with their passion for the log home lifestyle, the Wrightmans have brought True North to the forefront of log home technology and design. Their patented system is widely acclaimed in the log home industry and their reputation for outstanding quality and innovation has resulted in an impressive list of referrals and word-of-mouth sales. True North log homes can be found in most U.S. states, including Alaska, as well as Great Britain, Ireland, Continental Europe, Mexico, Korea, Bahamas, Japan and throughout Canada.

TODAY

As C.E.O., Rob is busy taking True North Log Homes from a family-run business to a reputable international company. He oversees a proficient management team that takes responsibility for the day-to-day operations of the company. Over the past 20 years, True North has grown from a small group of dedicated staff members to an employee group of close to 50 people, who share the Wrightmans' passion for the True North quality.

True North's relentless quest for improvement continues today, with the launch of a new product that will further enhance the performance of the True North technology. The patent-pending, Six-Seal System is another industry first and an example of the kind of research and creativity that keeps True North at the forefront among log home buyers.

SATISFIED CUSTOMERS KNOW BEST

The story of True North Log Homes is best expressed through the satisfaction of many True North log home owners. The company's commitment to providing the beauty and ambience of a traditional log home lifestyle, while integrating the latest in technology, has proven to be a winning combination.

"Ultimately, the knowledgeable staff, their passion for excellence, and the company's confidence in offering a 25-year "Zero" Air Infiltration Warranty made it clear to me that this was the log home I was searching for…I talked to several companies, but when it came down to it, True North stood out as the best choice"

– Maureen Campbell, Owner
Indian River Dream Bed, Breakfast and Spa, Muskoka, Ontario

Defining *Moments*

The True North Difference

Log homes have been built on this continent for centuries, from temporary cabins used by loggers and trappers to permanent homes and cottages. Some of the world's most luxurious hotels and vacation resorts have also used the natural beauty and ambience of logs to distinguish themselves from their competitors.

While honoring the history and heritage of log homes, True North Log Homes has developed a patented log home system that takes log home construction to a whole new level with the use of materials and joinery techniques unavailable to our forefathers. What True North has developed is the most technologically advanced log home in the world, one that embodies the superb craftsmanship of the past with the comfort and low maintenance demanded in a modern home. The following are just a few of the advantages and advanced technologies that separates True North Log Homes from all the others:

- **THE FINEST WOOD IN NORTH AMERICA** *(PAGE 196)*
- **BUTT SPLINE TECHNOLOGY** *(PAGE 197)*
- **SIX SEAL SYSTEM** *(PAGE 198)*
- **PRECISION CUT COMPUTER-CONTROLLED EQUIPMENT**
- **PENTA-POST CORNER SYSTEM** *(PAGE 199)*
- **KEYLOCK AIR SEAL CORNER**® *(PAGE 200)*
- **KEY SPLINE, POST SLIDE SYSTEM** *(PAGE 202)*
- **LOG LOCK COMPRESSION SYSTEM** *(PAGE 204)*
- **25-YEAR ZERO AIR INFILTRATION WARRANTY** *(PAGE 208)*

TRUE NORTH JOINERY TECHNOLOGY IS TRULY REVOLUTIONARY

Within the walls of every True North log home are many innovations, highlighted by an exclusive patented joinery system that is unmatched in the industry. At the heart of True North's innovations, which include 18 (soon to be 24) Canadian and U.S. patents, is the Keylock Air Seal Corner and the new LOG LOCK Compression System.

The dovetail on each True North log is precision cut using computer-controlled equipment, then joined to adjacent logs using patented polypropylene keylocks. The result is a corner that is unsurpassed in the industry; it is completely airtight and protected from water infiltration.

True North is the only log home manufacturer able to offer a 25-year "Zero" Air Infiltration Warranty. The Keylock Air Seal Corner® and LOG LOCK compression system are the key advantages of a True North log home. This technology ensures no chinking or exterior caulking will ever be needed on a True North log home.

True North takes full advantage of the naturally occurring shrinkage in the width and length of logs to make their homes airtight. The introduction of strategically placed patented keylocks, butt splines, tongue and groove systems and keysplines work with nature to actually tighten the log structure over time.

True North has revolutionized the first post to log, interlocking tongue and groove joinery system in log home construction. This penta post (5-sided post) joinery allows irregular wall angles to be part of your log home design. Turrets and prow fronts can easily become part of your design.

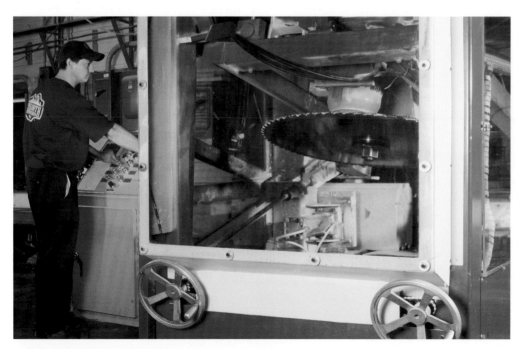

True North's dovetail machine, shown above, cuts the dovetail to precision in an impressive 33 seconds.

PRECISION MANUFACTURING

True North's construction of the world's largest heavy log wall, computer-aided manufacturing plant has brought log home building into the 21st century. True North homes are manufactured with such precision that the home need only be erected once – on your building site, resulting in substantial cost savings.

True North is at the top when it comes to quality construction, and they deserve to be there. The precision of their work and attention to details is outstanding – you know what you're getting with True North.

— T. Fagan, Fagan Construction

The True North plant is capable of producing a 2,000-square-foot home is less than eight hours. Each log wall is produced sequentially using computer-generated cutting drawings. All door and window openings are custom cut and all log lock, butt spline and keylock holes are pre-drilled. All material is finished to full measure in 6" x 12", 8" x 12", 10" x 12" and 12" x 12" (special order) sizes and milling is to a tolerance of 1/5,000th of an inch.

FIRST COAT OF STAIN

True North Log Homes is the first log home company in the world to provide a factory-applied primer stain. True North applies the first coat of stain to your logs to protect against airborne fungus and mildew during on-site construction.

True North's combination of quality materials, advanced technology and precision craftsmanship is what defines the True North difference. The True North log home is truly low maintenance and worry-free.

When you choose a True North log home, you enjoy the satisfaction of knowing you've not only built your dream home, but you've created a lifestyle that will provide a legacy for generations to remember.

Protecting
Your Investment

ACCURATE INVENTORY CONTROL

Every aspect of your True North log home is carefully monitored with a digital inventory control system that protects your log home from loss, damage or theft, from start to finish.

TRUE NORTH'S DIGITAL INVENTORY CONTROL SYSTEM HAS FOUR PARTS:

1. Detailed digital photographs are taken of all logs and log components, right down to the bolts and washers. Photographs are also taken of each individual piece, before and after they are packed on skids, to show both quality and quantity.

2. Photos are taken of the packed delivery truck, assuring all the lifts are packed, making note as to the shape and configuration of the truck.

3. Photos of the truck are taken again on the customer's site to ensure all the goods have arrived safely and that the configuration of the truck has not been altered in any way.

4. Photos of the lifts, with the customer's foundation in the background, are taken to provide a comfort level to the customer and to the customer's insurance company. This provides a visual track record to show that the goods have left the True North plant and arrived on the customer's site intact. Should the customer sustain theft on the site, it becomes a simple task to provide proof to the insurance company that all goods arrived on site in good order.

Our objective at True North is to deliver you value. With our digital inventory control system, you can be assured that you will receive everything as listed in your contract. You can enjoy the peace of mind that your house is being well managed and well cared for at every stage of design, delivery and construction.

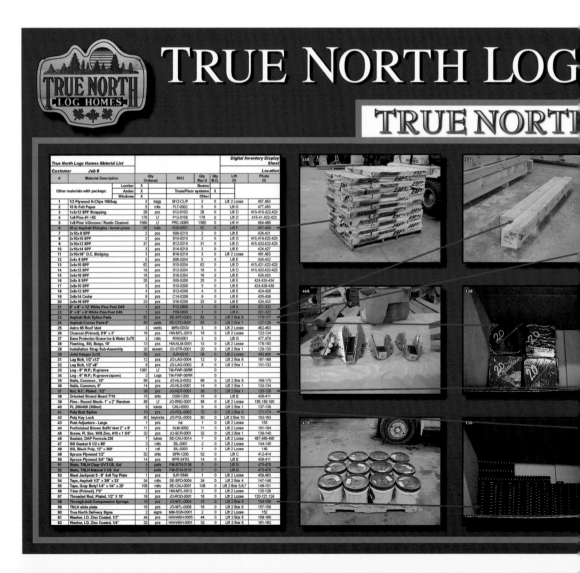

HOMES DIGITAL INVENTORY CONTROL SYSTEM

FACTORY

CUSTOMER SITE

Lift Control Sheet							Digital Inventory Display Sheet	
Customer	Job #							Location
#	Content	Length	Height	Width	Weight	Picture ID	Truck	Received
Lift 1	Log	14'10	3'4	4'0	5100	441	2	041
Lift 2	Components	4'0	3'4	4'0	5400	445	2	045
Lift 3	Log	12'5	3'4	4'0	3800	454	1	053
Lift 4	Log	12'11	3'4	4'0	3000	453	1	053
Lift 5	Log	16'6	3'4	4'0	5300	430	1	037
Lift 6	Log	12'7	3'4	4'0	3200	445	2	036
Lift 7	Log	11'3	3'4	4'0	3200	450	1	050
Lift 8	Log	14	3'4	4'0	4100	455	1	055
Lift 9	Log	21'5	3'4	4'0	1000	451	1	051
Lift 10	Log	10'2	3'4	4'0	900	451	1	051
				weight of log	35000			

#	Content	Length	Height	Width	Weight	Picture ID	Truck	Received
Skid A	siding	16'0	2'0	4'0	800	438	1	032
Skid B	5/8" plywood	16'0	3'0	4'0	2300	447	2	047
Skid C	OSB	16'0	2'0	4'0	1500	451	1	051
Skid D	5/8" plywood	8'0	3'0	4'0	2800	453	1	053
Skid E	Plywood, 1/2",3/4", 5/8	8'0	2'6	4'0	2000	449	1	049
Skid F	5/8" plywood	8'0	3'0	4'0	2200	444	2	043
Skid G	3/4" Plywood	8'0	3'0	4'0	2200	447	2	047
Skid H	2x6x10spf	10'0	3'0	4'0	3500	460	2	036
Skid I	2x4x10spf	8'0	3'0	4'0	2000	451	1	051
Skid J	1x4x16spf, 2x12x14spf, 2x8x8spf, 2x8x10spf	16'0	2'0	4'0	2600	453	1	053
Skid K	2x12x10spf, 2x8x8spf, 2x8x10spf	12'0	2'6	4'0	1800	447	2	047
Skid L	2x8x10spf, 2x8x12spf, 2x8x16spf	16'0	2'6	4'0	2600	456	2	056
Skid M	1x3x12strapping, 2x4x12spf, 2x6x10spf	12'0	2'6	4'0	2200	450	1	050
Skid N	2x12x16spf, 2x12x20spf, 2x12x22spf, 2x8x16spf	22'0	3'0	4'0	4300	454	1	051
Skid O	3/4" Plywood	10'0	3'0	4'0	2000	454	1	043
Skid P	plywood, 3/4", 5/8"	10'0	2'6	4'0	1200	443	1	046
Skid Q	1x6 v-groove,2x8x14cedar,	8'0	3'0	4'0	2200	455	1	055
Skid R	1x6 v-groove	16'0	3'0	4'0	3200	442	1	048
Skid S	1x9rustic channel, 1x8 #1#2pine	16'0	3'0	4'0	1800	444	2	042
Skid T	Stain	8'0	3'0	4'0	800	444	2	042
Skid U	Felt Paper	8'0	2'6	4'0	600	444	2	042
Skid V	Pine Posts	10'0	3'0	4'0	2000	454	1	054
Skid W	Pine Posts	10'0	3'0		3200	430		050
				weight of dimensional	50000		weight of Truck #1	Weight of Truck #2
				total weight	85000		42800	42200

Take a *Moment* to Learn About True North

WE BELIEVE OUR BEST CUSTOMER IS A WELL-INFORMED CUSTOMER.

True North offers regularly-scheduled informative seminars to demonstrate how a True North log home is built. The seminars have become very popular among prospective log home owners worldwide. Here is a first-hand account of the seminar experience from seminar participant, Kathy Hunt.

TRUE NORTH LOG HOMES FACTORY TOUR & CONSTRUCTION SEMINAR

I've always liked the idea of one day owning a custom-built log home. So I decided to attend True North's Construction Seminar to find out if their homes might be a good choice. I was joined by over 50 people, including Joan and Roy, who had driven 15 hours from Long Island, New York, to attend the seminar.

Joan and Roy had been researching log homes for almost ten years. When I met them at the True North Log Homes seminar, they had narrowed down their choice to True North and one other company. They had made the long drive from their home for the sole purpose of attending this seminar. I later found out that several of the seminar participants had travelled long distances to attend. I couldn't help thinking: there must be something special about these log homes that I didn't know!

While we were waiting for the seminar to begin, I toured the True North log home model with Joan and Roy. I found it pleasant to be surrounded by the logs, feeling the warmth of the wood. Joan and Roy, with their ten years of experience, were more observant. They immediately noticed the attention to detail and pointed out how well the windows and trim fit together within the log design. They pointed out the distinctive dovetail corners and the large size of the logs used in a True North home.

FAMILY-LED BUSINESS

The seminar got underway in the True North factory. We were surrounded by timber and large, computerized mill equipment. "This is the real thing!" I thought – so much more than any video tutorial about how a log home is built.

My second surprise came when I learned that the seminar leader, Rob Wrightman, was also the owner of the company. This is a true family business. I learned about his father, the inventor, and was impressed at how much Rob, as C.E.O., knew about building and how passionate he was about sharing his expertise. He not only had years of experience building log homes, but had also worked with his father to develop the technology.

The seminar followed the entire process of building a True North log home, – from the unique qualities of the forests that supply the timber, to the preparation and storage of the logs, to the computer precision of the joinery systems, to the actual construction of a corner section, to the digitally-controlled delivery system.

THIS IS THE HOME I WANT

I was completely captivated by the care and attention this company puts into their product. Their ongoing research into how to make a better product for their customer was evident at every stage of production. For example, they explained why they use an environmentally friendly water borne stain and why they are one of the only companies to apply a primer coat of stain to the logs at the factory.

About halfway through the seminar, I could clearly see the benefits of a True North log home, compared to any other kind of home. But, it wasn't until I witnessed the assembly of a joint section that I was truly amazed. One of the seminar participants was invited to hammer a three-log section together, demonstrating just how easily and efficiently the logs fit together. I could really see for myself how the technology worked, which seemed to be a combination of smart, simple physics combined with superior materials.

I left the seminar thinking that someday I would buy a True North log home and I'd be surprised if Joan and Roy didn't leave feeling the same. It was an enjoyable and extremely educational three hours, and even someone who didn't plan on becoming a True North customer, would have picked up invaluable information about how to choose a quality log home at this seminar.

TRUE NORTH SEMINARS SUPPORT THE HOSPITAL FOR SICK CHILDREN

Over the past 20 years, Rob has witnessed the challenges faced by children and their families at this hospital. Sometimes it has been while visiting friends and relatives, and on two occasions, involved instances where his sons had to be rushed to the hospital.

These experiences have had a profound affect on Rob. He vowed that he would develop a method to help the children and support the outstanding care provided by the Hospital for Sick Children (SickKids). Ultimately the True North seminars have provided the avenue to achieve this goal.

> *" People think that the problems we have in our everyday lives are huge and insurmountable, but they're not even in the same league as what these kids go through "*
>
> *– Robert A. Wrightman*

True North Log Homes is committed to supporting the Hospital for Sick Children in Toronto, Canada. True North donates all the registration fees received from seminar participants, which are matched dollar for dollar by True North, to the Hospital for Sick Children.

"THANK YOU TO ALL OF OUR SEMINAR PARTICIPANTS FOR HELPING US TO SUPPORT THE HOSPITAL FOR SICK CHILDREN."

ABOUT SICK KIDS...

The Hospital for Sick Children (SickKids), affiliated with the University of Toronto, is Canada's most research-intensive hospital and the largest centre in the country dedicated to improving children's health. As innovators in child health, SickKids improves the health of children by integrating care, research and teaching. To learn about how your donation helps, visit: *http://www.sickkidsfoundation.com/whygive/default.asp*

True North Log Homes also contributes to many other organizations that support children and/or health care, including Foster Parents Plan, South Asian Relief Fund and the Canadian Cancer Society, to name a few. True North is an active member of the local community and regularly participates in activities that support community services, such as the Bracebridge Rotary Club, Children's Foundation of Muskoka, South Muskoka Memorial Hospital Foundation and the Salvation Army.

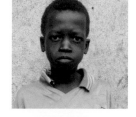

True North Log Homes owner, Rob Wrightman, along with his wife and sons, presents a donation to the Hospital for Sick Children in Toronto.

True North Log Homes is a proud supporter of Foster Parents Plan.

The popular True North Educational Seminar supports the company's philosophy that "our best customer is a well-informed customer."

Capture the *Moment*
Planning Your Home

" We are living in our own masterpiece! We actually designed much of the home ourselves, so we enjoy our great room and view of the mountains – everyday – that much more! "

— J. and R. Burgan, True North log home owners, Colorado

THE ADVENTURE BEGINS

Every True North log home begins with a dream – for a lifestyle that reflects your values and personality – in surroundings that inspire you.

The thrill of building a custom home begins with the design. Creating your own unique living space is what turns an ordinary house into an extraordinary lifestyle experience. At True North, our goal is to help you achieve this.

We offer you the choice of many popular True North designs, which can be built exactly as shown throughout this plan book, or with your own modifications. We have the expertise to help you make decisions that will realize your log home dream without compromising quality. Your True North representative has the experience and training to guide you through the entire design, planning and building process to make sure that your home becomes the "masterpiece" you have envisioned.

A STEP-BY-STEP PROCESS

1 – DESIGN DRAWINGS

When your drawing deposit is received, your True North representative documents the specific requirements and options of your home on a Project Information Sheet. This is then used to create small-scale (1/8") drawings of your home, which detail floor plans, foundation perimeter, elevations, roof detail, window and door placements. These drawings are modified as necessary to reflect your ideas and dreams. The objective is to create a meeting of the minds on paper. Once this is achieved, True North will have the information required to cost your project.

2 – CONTRACT PRESENTATION

Upon the signing and acceptance of design drawings, a contract price is established and presented, followed by contract signing and deposit.

3 – WORKING DRAWINGS

Sometimes referred to as blueprints, these drawings are based on the finalized design drawings and are used to obtain your building permit and to guide your builder in the construction of your home. At this stage, True North provides you with a Critical Timetable (C.T.T.) that outlines the payment, cutting and delivery schedules.

4 – CUT DRAWINGS AND CUTTING PROCESS

These are the drawings that are used by the True North factory to plan and cut your log home, and by your contractor to assemble the logs during construction. Upon acceptance and sign-off of the cut drawings, your cut payment is required. Your drawings are then forwarded to the factory to begin the cutting of your home. Simultaneously, the roof trusses, windows and other components of your home are ordered. Cut drawings show the courses of logs, their lengths and the window/door openings. The information on these drawings directly corresponds to the actual logs, which are labeled so they can be easily located and properly assembled during your building process.

5 – PACKING, DELIVERY AND FINAL PAYMENT

Your home and every component required for the build is packed in a systematic order, so that when your home is delivered, it arrives on-site with each lift containing the exact contents the builder requires in the proper order of the build. This saves time and money on-site by eliminating the task of sorting materials. During packing, a digital inventory control system is used to assure that every item is accounted for and that quality is not compromised. You will be asked for final payment before delivery is made to your site.

6 – FOLLOW UP

True North oversees the delivery, and in many instances, the construction of your new home. Over the course of the build, we will contact you on a regular basis to ensure the process is going smoothly and to help with any issues or difficulties that may arise.

The Citadel, True North's flagship home, is a designer showcase with many innovative design features. The new patent-pending distinctive timber frame kingpost (optional) and classic turret provide a stunning octagonal interior space with options for flat, partial or full cathedral ceiling profiles. A living room projection with interior ceiling features and exposed log corner dovetails make the great room perfect for entertaining and showcasing your lake, forest and rocky mountain vistas.

True North's patent pending Kingpost is just one of the many custom features to be found in this home.

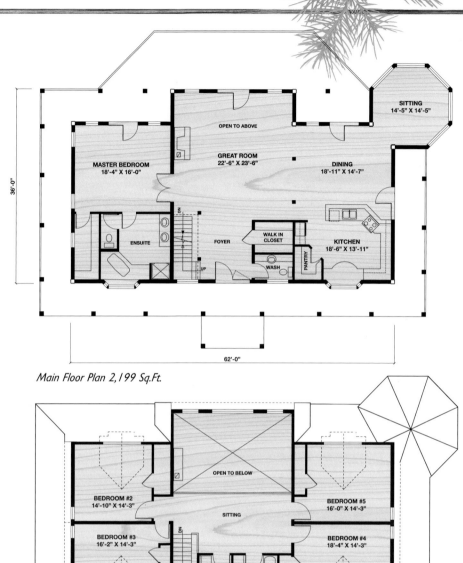

Main Floor Plan 2,199 Sq.Ft.

Second Floor Plan 1,584 Sq.Ft.

*T*his designer home is the ultimate in relaxation! This is where the homeowner can savour life's best moments and enjoy "down time" with family and friends. As a lakeside retreat, the home was designed to take advantage of the outdoor vistas from the many special indoor and outdoor seating areas.

Citadel
I

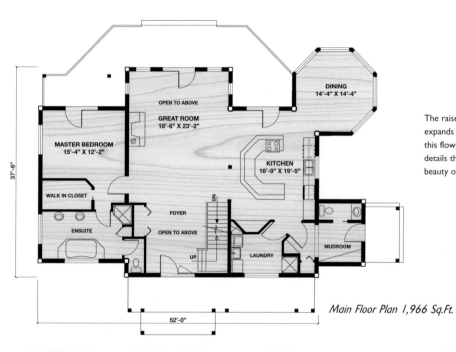

MASTER BEDROOM
15'-4" X 12'-2"

OPEN TO ABOVE

GREAT ROOM
18'-6" X 23'-2"

DINING
14'-4" X 14'-4"

KITCHEN
16'-9" X 19'-5"

WALK IN CLOSET

FOYER

OPEN TO ABOVE

ENSUITE

DN

UP

LAUNDRY

MUDROOM

37'-6"

52'-0"

Main Floor Plan 1,966 Sq.Ft.

The raised wrap-around deck expands the living space of this flowing design home with details that blend into the natural beauty of the surroundings.

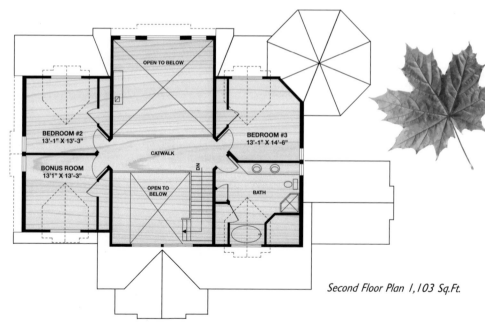

OPEN TO BELOW

BEDROOM #2
13'-1" X 13'-3"

CATWALK

BEDROOM #3
13'-1" X 14'-6"

BONUS ROOM
13'1" X 13'-3"

DN

OPEN TO BELOW

BATH

Second Floor Plan 1,103 Sq.Ft.

*L*iving in this True North home is like living in a work of art. It is designed to provide a peaceful oasis from a hectic pace of life – a place for creating warm memories that will always be cherished.

Citadel II

DINING 15'-8" X 15'-8"

OPEN TO ABOVE

GREAT ROOM 20'-2" X 24'-7"

ENSUITE

MASTER BEDROOM 15'-2" X 14'-0"

KITCHEN 16'-0" X 21'-7"

WASH

WALK IN CLOSET

POWDER

LINEN

OPEN TO ABOVE

FOYER

UP

ENTRANCE

LAUNDRY

PANTRY

38'-0"

54'-0"

GARAGE

Main Floor Plan 2,192 Sq.Ft.
Garage 1,332 Sq.Ft.

OPEN TO BELOW

BEDROOM #2 13'-3" X 13'-11"

BEDROOM #4 13'-6" X 13'-11"

BEDROOM #3 13'-3" X 13'-11"

OPEN TO BELOW

BATH

COMMON ROOM

GARAGE BED #1

WASH

WASH

GARAGE BED #2

DN

Second Floor Plan 1,117 Sq.Ft.
Garage Apartment 1,270 Sq.Ft.

A studio apartment with a unique walk-out balcony is located just above the garage.

*O*ur Citadel is delightful for so many reasons. In addition to the many creative design features, our home's open concept is what we enjoy the most. It is ideal for entertaining and other celebrations.
— R. and M. Wrightman,
True North homeowners, Muskoka, Ontario

Citadel III

A peek through the dovetailed
entry reveals the stunning style, texture and
colours of the wooden floor, walls and ceiling
that exude extraordinary warmth and ambience.

Casual dining is pure pleasure under a
turret of light and beams in this octagonal space.

Water, wood, tile and windows will pamper your senses.

Sink deep into a luxurious bath with your own private view to the world outside.

Bedroom bliss awaits your guests after sharing an evening in the great outdoors.

The patent pending Kingpost commands your attention as you pass over the walkway connecting the upper bedrooms and bath.

Life is not measured by the number
of breaths you take, but by the
moments that take your breath away.

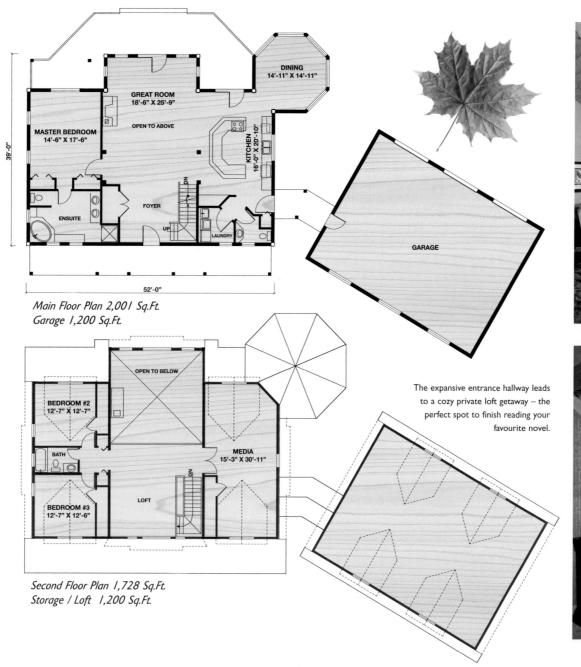

DINING
14'-11" X 14'-11"

GREAT ROOM
18'-6" X 25'-9"

OPEN TO ABOVE

MASTER BEDROOM
14'-6" X 17'-6"

KITCHEN
16'-0" X 20'-10"

ENSUITE

FOYER

DN

UP

LAUNDRY

GARAGE

39'-0"

52'-0"

Main Floor Plan 2,001 Sq.Ft.
Garage 1,200 Sq.Ft.

OPEN TO BELOW

BEDROOM #2
12'-7" X 12'-7"

BATH

BEDROOM #3
12'-7" X 12'-6"

LOFT

MEDIA
15'-3" X 30'-11"

DN

Second Floor Plan 1,728 Sq.Ft.
Storage / Loft 1,200 Sq.Ft.

The expansive entrance hallway leads
to a cozy private loft getaway – the
perfect spot to finish reading your
favourite novel.

This is the log home for anyone who appreciates perfection! If you can't find the perfect home - then build the perfect home. It's hard to find a log home that combines elegance, warmth and personality. True North made this a home we love to come home to!

— M. & S. Kramer, True North homeowner, North Carolina.

Citadel
IV

This master ensuite with antique corner tub, vanity and velvet chair adds a luxurious feminine touch.

The long granite island counter is a welcome spot for friends to chat and laugh with the chef who may be preparing the catch of the day.

Friends often gather in this wild and wonderful great room to share plans for the next hunting trip, while a mammoth elk head protrudes from the fireplace as a reminder of a successful trip's trophy.

The distinctive patterns of the bedroom décor contrast with the soothing warmth of the logs.

A hanging antler chandelier sheds light on the conversation while enjoying a meal in the turreted dining room.

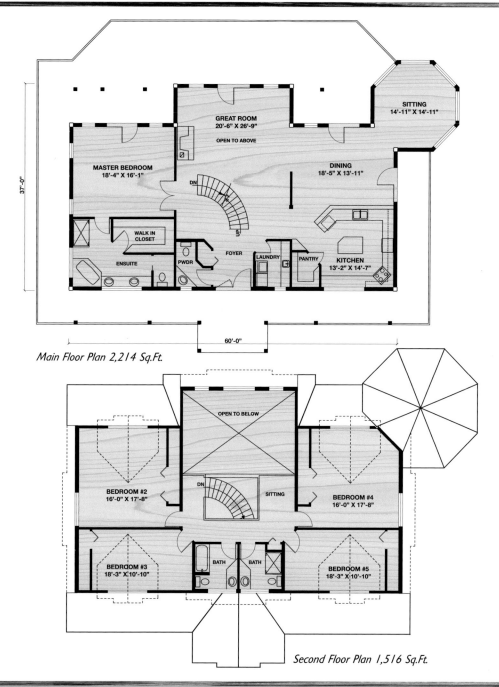

Main Floor Plan 2,214 Sq.Ft.

Second Floor Plan 1,516 Sq.Ft.

A curved log staircase of white pine timber adds dramatic effect to the stylish contours of this home.

If you have ever dreamed about a log home — owning one is a thousand times better! Working with True North's designers and engineers was a wonderful experience — they made our dreams a reality. Guests are amazed at our home's design, especially the "Kingpost" technology used to support the roof.

— B. and M. McLay, True North homeowners, Muskoka, Ontario

Citadel V

This hand-crafted bed is the next best thing to sleeping and dreaming outdoors.

The massive moose head is sure to be a topic of wilderness adventure stories while relaxing in front of the stone fireplace.

A popular meeting area is the kitchen with dining space and vintage wines.

Lovingly crafted wood provides angled entries into the upstairs bedrooms with separate baths and a small sitting area overlooking the great room.

Main Floor Plan 1,998 Sq.Ft.

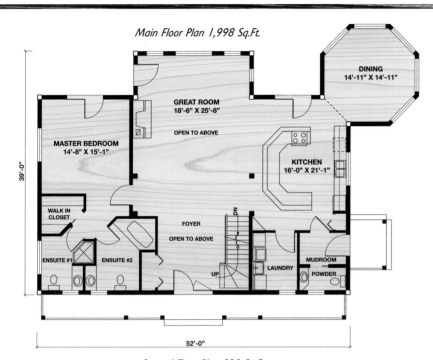

DINING
14'-11" X 14'-11"

GREAT ROOM
18'-6" X 25'-8"
OPEN TO ABOVE

MASTER BEDROOM
14'-8" X 15'-1"

KITCHEN
16'-0" X 21'-1"

39'-0"

WALK IN
CLOSET

FOYER
OPEN TO ABOVE

DN

MUDROOM

ENSUITE #1   ENSUITE #2   UP   LAUNDRY   POWDER

52'-0"

Second Floor Plan 928 Sq.Ft.

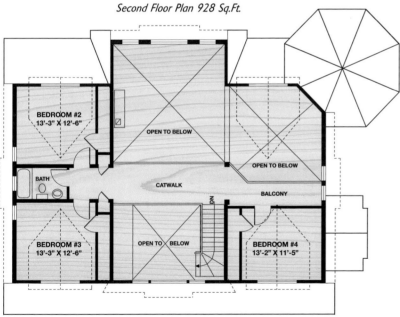

BEDROOM #2
13'-3" X 12'-6"

OPEN TO BELOW

OPEN TO BELOW

BATH

CATWALK   BALCONY

BEDROOM #3
13'-3" X 12'-6"

OPEN TO BELOW   DN

BEDROOM #4
13'-2" X 11'-5"

The warmth and beauty of natural stone, a one-of-a-kind hand-woven rug and a wood interior with cathedral ceiling creates an unforgettable ambience.

The design of our True North home is just awesome. The great room is our absolute favourite. The views from the soaring windows are simply spectacular. Our building adventure, from start to finish with True North, was a wonderful and easy experience. — M. and E. Ziraldo, True North homeowners, Apsley, Ontario

Citadel VI

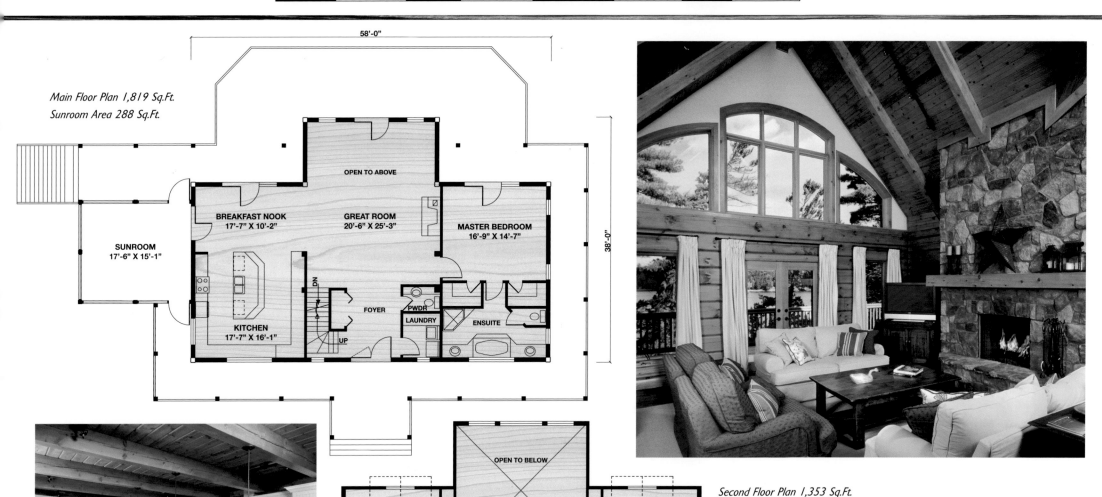

Main Floor Plan 1,819 Sq.Ft.

Sunroom Area 288 Sq.Ft.

58'-0"

38'-0"

OPEN TO ABOVE

BREAKFAST NOOK
17'-7" X 10'-2"

GREAT ROOM
20'-6" X 25'-3"

MASTER BEDROOM
16'-9" X 14'-7"

SUNROOM
17'-6" X 15'-1"

DN

UP

FOYER

PWDR

LAUNDRY

ENSUITE

KITCHEN
17'-7" X 16'-1"

OPEN TO BELOW

Second Floor Plan 1,353 Sq.Ft.

BEDROOM #2
15'-2" X 13'-4"

BEDROOM #4
15'-2" X 13'-4"

CATWALK

BEDROOM #3
15'-2" X 13'-4"

DN

BEDROOM #5
15'-2" X 13'-4"

BATH   BATH

White kitchen cabinetry, black chairs, gleaming counter tops and stainless steel appliances add a rich textural mix to compliment the floor and log beams.

*W*e absolutely love our cottage. It's a great family getaway where we can escape from our busy lives and relax with the children. True North was able to help us design a lakeside retreat with a rustic and elegant look that matches the beauty and majesty of our location.
— D. and P Webster,
True North homeowners, Lake Rosseau, Ontario

Citadel VII

The Huntingford is grand, spacious and open –
for living at your home-on-the range property
or high upon a cliff overlooking lakes.
The Huntingford features a large great room
with floor-to-ceiling stone fireplace and windows
reaching skywards. A wrap around porch is
available and can hug the outside of the home
to make you feel as close to Mother Nature as
possible.

MASTER BEDROOM
14'-8" X 19'-2"

CATHEDRAL CEILING

WALK IN CLOSET

ENSUITE

SCREENED PORCH

LIVING
23'-2" X 18'-10"
OPEN TO ABOVE

KITCHEN
16'-0" X 17'-10"

CATHEDRAL CEILING

DINING
20'-0" X 15'-8"

LAUNDRY
9'-10" X 8'-7"

SCREENED PORCH

FOYER
14'-8" X 13'-0"

SERVICE

BATH

OFFICE
10'-9" X 10'-6"

BEDROOM #2
14'-8" X 10'-9"

68'-1"

73'-6"

Main Floor Plan 2,550 Sq.Ft.

Second Floor Plan 425 Sq.Ft.

CATHEDRAL CEILING

OPEN TO BELOW

CATHEDRAL CEILING

LOFT
24'-1" X 16'-6"

DN

Leaving the kitchen may be difficult when the chef can enjoy such spectacular lake views while preparing a meal from the kitchen island.

*W*e wanted a family retreat on the shores of this wonderful lake that had the look and feel of a cabin built long ago. True North Log Homes and our builder gave us just what we wanted — we are very pleased. —True North homeowner, Quebec

Huntingford I

The pyramid shaped hearth, developed from locally sourced material, features a stacked-stone design style that is difficult to achieve. The pine floor is made of reclaimed lumber from local river logs.

A perfect corner niche with a view provides a perfect area for a night of fun and games.

Enter the dining room to step back in time and enjoy a savory meal.

A grand foyer and front deck provide stunning views to the outside.

No excuses here, no matter the weather, the exercise loft encourages you to enjoy the sky-high view while working out.

This magnificent vacation property, nestled among ancient pine forests, oversees the serenity of the lake and mountains, while providing all the comforts of a traditional wilderness lodge.

54'-0"

28'-0"

ENSUITE

WALK THRU CLOSET

WASH

OPEN TO ABOVE

FOYER

UP

DN

KITCHEN
14'-0" X 17'-6"

MUDROOM

UP

GARAGE

MASTER BEDROOM
15'-7" X 15'-0"

LIVING
19'-4" X 22'-7"

DINING
17'-0" X 9'-0"

OPEN TO ABOVE

Main Floor Plan 1,657 Sq.Ft.
Garage & Mudroom 974 Sq.Ft.

Kids count in the design of this home – with a rec room over the garage, attached by a deck to the main house,

The practical working kitchen is conveniently located next to the main living area.

ATTIC

OPEN TO BELOW

ATTIC

BATH

DN

LOFT
22'-2" X 14'-7"

BEDROOM #2
15'-9" X 15'-2"

BEDROOM #3
14'-0" X 15'-2"

OPEN TO BELOW

GARAGE LOFT

DN

Second Floor Plan 934 Sq.Ft.
Garage Loft 848 Sq.Ft.

*W*e turned what once was a small cabin on the family property into our dream home. We now enjoy our heritage property year round and in much more comfortable surroundings! — J. and C. Nedoroski, True North homeowners, Minnesota

Huntingford II

A wall of windows provide picturesque lake views when friends gather around the cozy, custom-designed stone and granite fireplace with arched opening.

A spacious entrance hallway to allow for the busy coming and going of children and all of their gear.

54'-0"

37'-0"

KITCHEN
15'-10" X 16'-11"

FOYER

POWDER

ENSUITE

LINEN

OPEN TO ABOVE

UP

PANTRY

WALK IN CLOSET

DN

DINING
15'-10" X 9'-7"

MASTER BEDROOM
15'-11" X 11'-8"

OPEN TO ABOVE

GREAT ROOM
18'-6" X 17'-11"

Main Floor Plan 1,680 Sq.Ft.

A covered porch was added to compliment the attractive features of the roofline with dormers and the bay window.

The French country décor accents the hues of the wood floors, walls and large ceiling timbers in the kitchen and dining area.

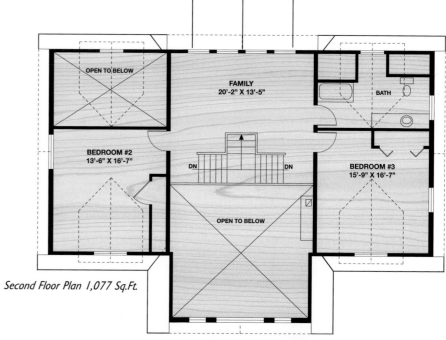

OPEN TO BELOW

FAMILY
20'-2" X 13'-5"

BATH

BEDROOM #2
13'-6" X 16'-7"

DN   **DN**

BEDROOM #3
15'-9" X 16'-7"

OPEN TO BELOW

Second Floor Plan 1,077 Sq.Ft.

*B*eing in a natural log home near the woods has enriched our lives. We love being out of the city and enjoy waking up to a natural setting. We are very impressed with the precision and quality of the True North logs and delivery was done with ease. We wouldn't change a thing about our home. R. and S. Kowal, True North homeowners, Minnesota

Huntingford III

56'-0" 24'-0"

24'-0"

OFFICE
13'-10" X 15'-8"

FOYER
6'-11" X 16'-0"

BATH

MUD ROOM
6'-11"X15'-8"

ENSUITE

GARAGE
23'-6" X 23'-0"

MASTER BEDROOM
21'-2" X 14'-3"

CATHEDRAL CEILING

WALK-IN
CLOSET

UP DN

KITCHEN
15'-10" X 14'-10"

GREAT ROOM
17'-1" X 22'-9"

OPEN TO ABOVE

DINING
15'-10" X 12'-0"

Main Floor Plan 1,930 Sq.Ft.
Garage 575 Sq.Ft.

BALCONY

WALK IN
CLOSET

BEDROOM #2
15'-11" X 15'-7"

BATH

STORAGE

CATHEDRAL CEILING

BEDROOM #3
23'-6" X 23'-0"

DN

OPEN TO BELOW

Second Floor Plan 1,520 Sq.Ft.

*O*ur home has turned the original family farm into a slice of heaven. We love the wood and the open floor plan that takes full advantage of our million-dollar view. Living here is like being on permanent vacation. We fell in love with the True North product. It is superior. — J. and C. Vadeboncoeur, True North homeowners, Georgia

Huntingford IV

The exquisite cedar railing, hand-cut, peeled and crafted by mother and daughter from cedar trees found on the original family property, overlooks the kitchen and living room area.

The fireplace features a hand-cut section of an old black walnut tree from the family property.

The great room highlights trophies, including this 40-pound Muskie,
dwarfed on the massive floor-to-ceiling fireplace.
Sky-high, wall-to-wall windows bring Mother Nature closer,
with lake views on all three sides and from every room,
including the main floor master bedroom, with ensuite.

Main Floor Plan 1,461 Sq.Ft.
Garage & Mudroom 907 Sq.Ft.

GARAGE
27'-0" X 27'-1"

MUDROOM

KITCHEN
16'-2" X 12'-8"

FOYER

ENSUITE

47'-6"

28'-0"

DINING
12'-1" X 13'-10"

DN

UP

MASTER BEDROOM
11'-9" X 16'-10"

GREAT ROOM
21'-9" X 18'-6"

OPEN TO ABOVE

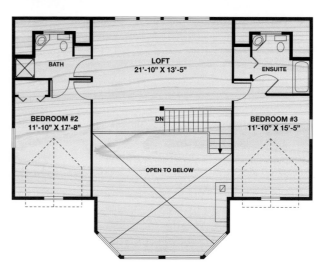

LOFT
21'-10" X 13'-5"

BATH

ENSUITE

BEDROOM #2
11'-10" X 17'-8"

DN

BEDROOM #3
11'-10" X 15'-5"

OPEN TO BELOW

Second Floor Plan 1,072 Sq.Ft.

We love the soothing fragrance of the pine and the warmth. We are situated high above the lake, ten miles from one of the coldest spots in the country. Our fuel bills are next to nothing. True North's full size logs, along with triple pane windows, are the best insulation you can find. — B. and B. Nelson, True North homeowners, Minnesota

Huntingford V

The loft provides the perfect getaway spot for some indoor games or the Sunday crossword challenge.

Designed as a gathering place for family, friends and "Fido," the wildlife décor gives the dining area a "cabin" feel.

Guests choose their favourite hand-carved log seats, while the host uses an island cook stove to prepare food and still be a part of everything – including the conversation and the outside views.

TRUE NORTH
LOG HOMES INC.

The Segwun surrounds you with a cozy elegance that is so inviting, so peaceful, that you feel like curling up on the couch to read or sharing a special evening with friends. The Segwun, with exposed interior log corner dovetails, takes you back to the simplicity and beauty of a bygone era. Choose the one-story model with main floor bedroom or add a loft where family and visitors can enjoy your sanctuary in the forest.

THE *Segwun* COLLECTION

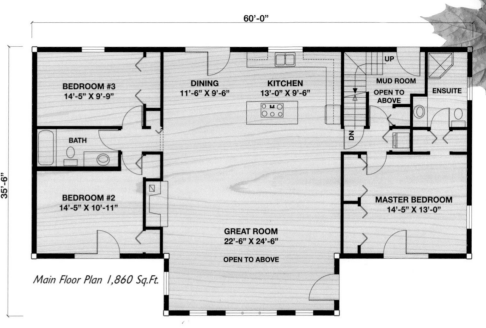

60'-0"

35'-6"

BEDROOM #3
14'-5" X 9'-9"

DINING
11'-6" X 9'-6"

KITCHEN
13'-0" X 9'-6"

UP

MUD ROOM
OPEN TO ABOVE

ENSUITE

BATH

DN

BEDROOM #2
14'-5" X 10'-11"

MASTER BEDROOM
14'-5" X 13'-0"

GREAT ROOM
22'-6" X 24'-6"

OPEN TO ABOVE

Main Floor Plan 1,860 Sq.Ft.

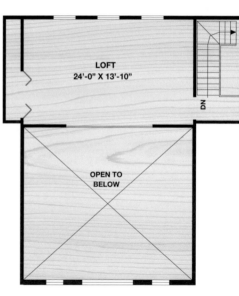

LOFT
24'-0" X 13'-10"

DN

OPEN TO BELOW

Second Floor Plan 405 Sq.Ft.

The warmth and ambience of a log home just seems to encapsulate you. We feel like we're coming home to a resort every night. Home is where the heart is and our True North log home truly meets all of our needs and wants. — J. J. Serre, True North homeowner, Alliston, Ontario

Seg'wun
I

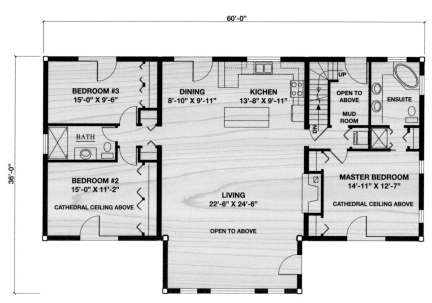

60'-0"

36'-0"

BEDROOM #3
15'-0" X 9'-6"

DINING
8'-10" X 9'-11"

KICHEN
13'-8" X 9'-11"

OPEN TO
ABOVE

ENSUITE

MUD
ROOM

BATH

BEDROOM #2
15'-0" X 11'-2"

CATHEDRAL CEILING ABOVE

LIVING
22'-6" X 24'-6"

OPEN TO ABOVE

MASTER BEDROOM
14'-11" X 12'-7"

CATHEDRAL CEILING ABOVE

Main Floor Plan 1,856 Sq.Ft.

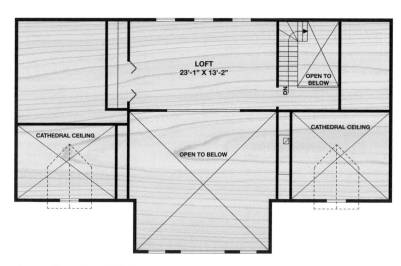

LOFT
23'-1" X 13'-2"

OPEN TO
BELOW

CATHEDRAL CEILING

OPEN TO BELOW

CATHEDRAL CEILING

Second Floor Plan 424 Sq.Ft.

Dormers in each bedroom add light, while providing the perfect inset for ceiling fans.

Our log home is more than we could ever have imagined! We enjoyed every part of our log home building experience. True North is so wonderful to work with, accommodating all of our ideas from start to finish.

— D. and L. Papple, True North homeowners, Muskoka, Ontario

Seg'wun II

A luxurious spa feeling is created in the bathroom with walk-in shower, reproduction claw tub and tumbled marble flooring with radiant heating.

Custom closets in the bedroom prevent clutter and keep the entertainment center hidden – until it's time to light the fire, grab the remote and relax.

Brazilian cherry wood and slate flooring in the kitchen area are just a few examples of the all-natural products featured in this home.

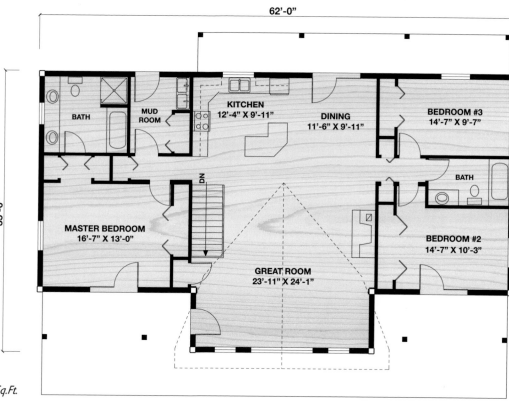

The exposed log corner dovetails, arched windows and cathedral ceilings in the Great Room show off the majesty of Mother Nature.

Owners and guests will be inspired to greet the day outside, because every bedroom, including this master, has its own private deck.

Main Floor Plan 1,916 Sq.Ft.

62'-0"

35'-6"

BATH

MUD ROOM

KITCHEN
12'-4" X 9'-11"

DINING
11'-6" X 9'-11"

BEDROOM #3
14'-7" X 9'-7"

BATH

MASTER BEDROOM
16'-7" X 13'-0"

DN

GREAT ROOM
23'-11" X 24'-1"

BEDROOM #2
14'-7" X 10'-3"

*W*e love the look and feeling of our home. There's something comforting about living in a log house that you don't get in conventional homes — it's as if we have a camaraderie with the logs. The True North logs and construction technology is fantastic. — P. and N. Cronk, True North homeowners, Minnesota

Segwun III

This home easily lives up to the adventurous spirit of the Klondike with its distinctively rugged design. The magnificent trapezoidal window design in the great room adds a stylish flair to this eye-catching home. The expansive wall of windows can be a flat or prow front, which not only enhances panoramic views, but also greatly increases the living and dining area of this attractive home.

THE Klondike COLLECTION

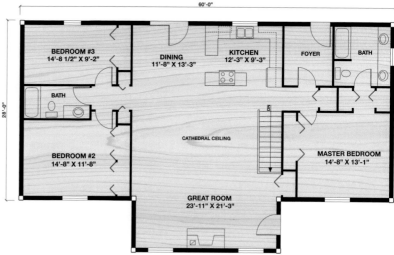

Main Floor Plan 1,865 Sq.Ft.

So simple, so elegant – the open living area,
with warmth from the fireplace, invites casual
get-togethers before or after dinner.

$\mathcal{T}$he Klondike design is an ideal vacation home, with large windows in
the living room for viewing the lake and a cozy fireplace centrepiece.

Klondike
I

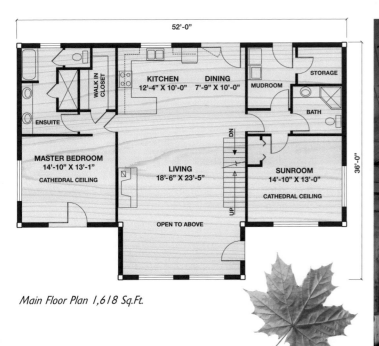

Main Floor Plan 1,618 Sq.Ft.

52'-0"

KITCHEN
12'-4" X 10'-0"

DINING
7'-9" X 10'-0"

STORAGE

MUDROOM

BATH

WALK IN CLOSET

ENSUITE

MASTER BEDROOM
14'-10" X 13'-1"
CATHEDRAL CEILING

LIVING
18'-6" X 23'-5"

SUNROOM
14'-10" X 13'-0"
CATHEDRAL CEILING

OPEN TO ABOVE

DN

UP

36'-0"

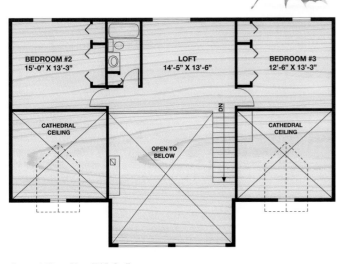

Second Floor Plan 745 Sq.Ft.

BEDROOM #2
15'-0" X 13'-3"

LOFT
14'-5" X 13'-6"

BEDROOM #3
12'-6" X 13'-3"

CATHEDRAL CEILING

CATHEDRAL CEILING

OPEN TO BELOW

DN

The bedroom doors swing open to a private walk-out for enjoying moonlit views of the lake before snuggling-in for the night.

The stone hearth in the great room beckons the whole family inside after enjoying an invigorating day on the lake.

The design of our home resembles a wonderful bed and breakfast we visited on the north shores of Lake Superior. Family members and grandkids enjoy spending time here all year long. We really like the way the True North logs fit together and weather so well. — G. and K. Waldon, True North homeowners, Minnesota

Klondike II

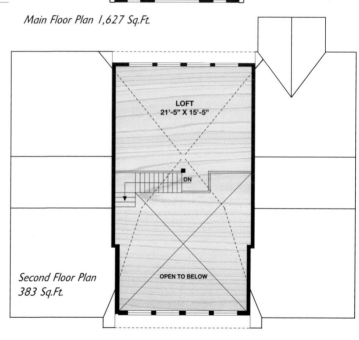

Main Floor Plan 1,627 Sq.Ft.

Second Floor Plan 383 Sq.Ft.

Instead of a staircase, this optional library-style ladder on wheels provides easy access to the large guest loft without taking up a lot of space in the great room.

*O*ur home was designed as a gathering place for our entire family, including our grandchildren and two large dogs. We're extremely pleased with how our home has made our get-togethers so much fun. The choice of True North was the best decision we made. We are very happy with the outcome. – L. and F. Beauchamp, True North homeowners, Ottawa

Klondike III

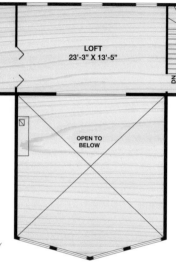

Main Floor Plan 1,999 Sq.Ft.

Second Floor Plan 402 Sq.Ft.

A beamed ceiling creates a comfy setting for casual kitchen eat-ins for friends and family.

*W*e are living in our own masterpiece and enjoy our great room with a view of the mountains everyday. True North stood out from the many log home companies we looked at and we were extremely pleased with their assistance — from the design stage right through to the completion. *— J. and R. Burgan, True North homeowners, Colorado*

Klondike IV

The Louisburg reflects its French Canadian inspiration through soaring majestic bell curve rooflines and eye-catching trademark dormers. The second floor is built into the roof design, which maximizes floor area and minimizes costs per square foot, making it a very popular model among log homebuyers. An expansive wrap-around porch is an added highlight to this appealing plan.

THE Louisburg COLLECTION

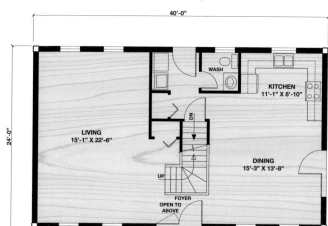

Main Floor Plan 960 Sq.Ft.

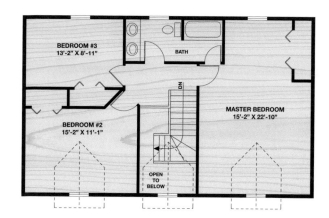

Second Floor Plan 865 Sq.Ft.

The centre staircase beautifully separates the casual dining/kitchen area from the living area and fireplace.

This home is the "flagship" of the True North Louisburg design series, which is known for its charming French Canadian appearance. The optional bellcurve roofline, dormers and broad covered veranda highlight this appealing design.

Louisburg I

A country kitchen motif fits perfectly into the French Canadian feel of this classic Louisburg.

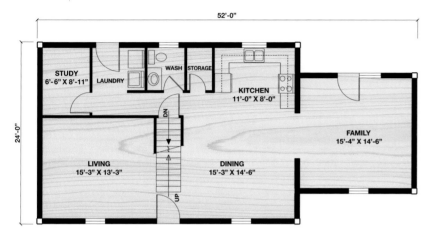

52'-0"

24'-0"

STUDY
6'-6" X 8'-11"

LAUNDRY

WASH

STORAGE

KITCHEN
11'-0" X 8'-0"

DN

UP

LIVING
15'-3" X 13'-3"

DINING
15'-3" X 14'-6"

FAMILY
15'-4" X 14'-6"

Main Floor Plan 1,120 Sq.Ft.

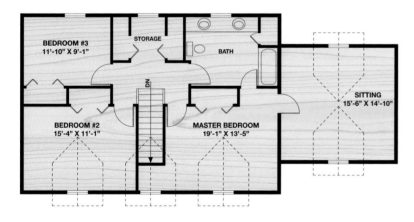

BEDROOM #3
11'-10" X 9'-1"

STORAGE

BATH

DN

BEDROOM #2
15'-4" X 11'-1"

MASTER BEDROOM
19'-1" X 13'-5"

SITTING
15'-6" X 14'-10"

Second Floor Plan 1,086 Sq.Ft.

This Louisburg was designed to compliment the vistas of a rocky lakefront property. Morning coffee can be savoured from the covered veranda, while sunsets can be enjoyed in the evening from the second floor optional deck.

Louisburg
II

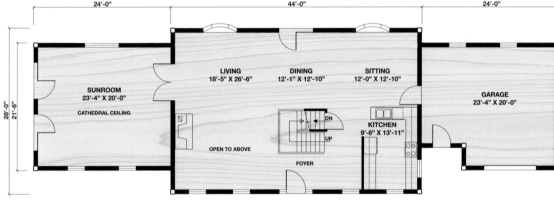

Main Floor Plan 1,748 Sq.Ft. Garage 483 Sq.Ft.

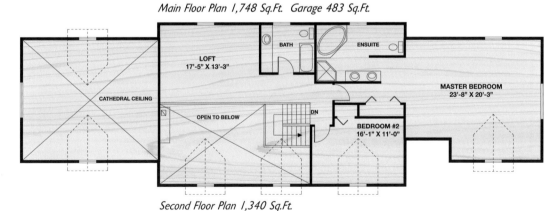

Second Floor Plan 1,340 Sq.Ft.

*W*ith over 3,000 square feet of living space, our family enjoys a home that is very spacious, yet cozy at the same time. Our friends continually comment on the warm, comfortable atmosphere in our home. It's great to have a place where everyone feels at home. — K. & A. Atkin, True North homeowner, Muskoka, Ontario

Louisburg III

48'-0"

40'-0"

ENSUITE

WALK IN CLOSET

WASH

ENTRY

LAUNDRY

KITCHEN
13'-4" X 9'-7"

DN

UP

MASTER BEDROOM
12'-11" X 18'-1"

OPEN TO ABOVE

OPEN TO ABOVE

DINING
13'-4" X 12'-3"

LIVING
18'-6" X 24'-6"

Main Floor Plan 1,640 Sq.Ft.

The upper loft includes an additional sleeping area and library for guests and family members.

Second Floor Plan 898 Sq.Ft.

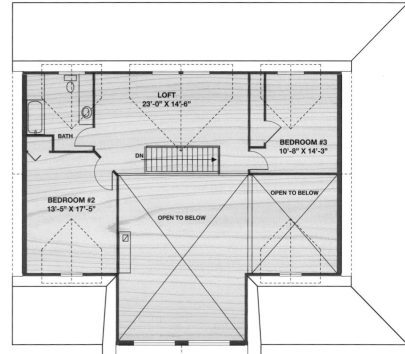

LOFT
23'-0" X 14'-6"

BATH

BEDROOM #3
10'-8" X 14'-3"

DN

BEDROOM #2
13'-5" X 17'-5"

OPEN TO BELOW

OPEN TO BELOW

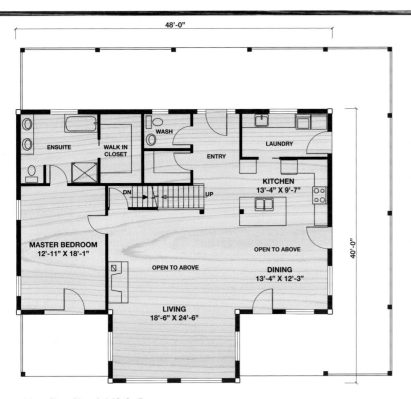

*W*e were attracted to this home because of the way it blends into nature, yet stands out with its own personality. We enjoy the panoramic views of the North Carolina mountains and our wrap-around decks, which become living rooms and even extra bedrooms during the summer. — D. Avery, True North homeowner, Georgia

Louisburg IV

The chandelier adds a touch of elegance to the varied shades and textures
of the rugged wood that surrounds you in comfort from floor to ceiling.

A hearth of stone with wood mantel displays a local
artist's palette of a view captured outside the home.

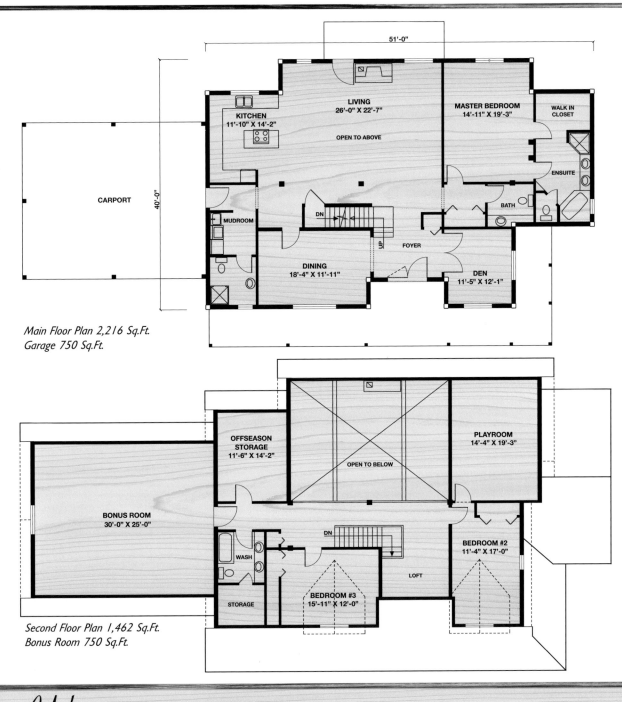

51'-0"

40'-0"

KITCHEN
11'-10" X 14'-2"

LIVING
26'-0" X 22'-7"

OPEN TO ABOVE

MASTER BEDROOM
14'-11" X 19'-3"

WALK IN CLOSET

ENSUITE

CARPORT

MUDROOM

DN

UP

BATH

DINING
18'-4" X 11'-11"

FOYER

DEN
11'-5" X 12'-1"

Main Floor Plan 2,216 Sq.Ft.
Garage 750 Sq.Ft.

OFFSEASON STORAGE
11'-6" X 14'-2"

OPEN TO BELOW

PLAYROOM
14'-4" X 19'-3"

BONUS ROOM
30'-0" X 25'-0"

WASH

DN

BEDROOM #2
11'-4" X 17'-0"

STORAGE

BEDROOM #3
15'-11" X 12'-0"

LOFT

Second Floor Plan 1,462 Sq.Ft.
Bonus Room 750 Sq.Ft.

Stainless steel appliances and black granite counter tops and table enhance the beauty of the kitchen beams and cabinetry.

We love the spaciousness, peacefulness and warmth of our casually elegant home. We decided not to paint at all, once we saw the beauty of the interior logs. We shopped around a lot before we purchased. The quality of True North is unsurpassed, with the best logs and the best building system.

— J. and J. Southerland,
True North homeowners, Arkansas

Louisburg V

The loft balcony includes two bedrooms with dormers, a four piece bathroom and angled walls to maximize easy access and privacy for all. The loft leads to the grandkids' playroom and a sitting area at the other end.

The master bedroom includes a bathroom ensuite with black fixtures which, compliment the varied colour hues of the natural logs.

The large open living room with exposed beams combines dark oak flooring with Arkansas yellow tongue and groove knotty pine ceilings to accentuate the warm hues of the logs.

THE MacKenzie COLLECTION

The Mackenzie offers the ultimate in comfort for everyday living. Relax and enjoy the view through the high trapezoidal windows in the open living room area while lounging in front of the stone hearth. The Mackenzie offers the convenience of single-floor living, while boasting a large cathedral ceiling in the great room. All amenities are available on the main floor, including the private master bedroom wing, accessed from the foyer. Overnight guests can choose to sleep in the large main-floor guest bedroom or retire to the luxury loft with a view.

46'-0"

34'-0"

BATH

BEDROOM #2
9'-11" X 10'-0"

KITCHEN
9'-4" X 9'-2"

FOYER

MASTER BEDROOM
12'-7" X 17'-0"

DN   UP

BATH

DINING
10'-7" X 13'-0"

OPEN TO ABOVE

LIVING
12'-0" X 13'-0"

Main Floor Plan 1,223 Sq.Ft.

The pronounced entry adds a touch of elegance to this distinctive vacation property.

STORAGE

BEDROOM #3
15'-0" X 13'-1"

STORAGE

DN

OPEN TO BELOW

Second Floor Plan 447 Sq.Ft.

Country dining with comfortable upholstery offers delightful views and the opportunity to head outside to the deck for an aperitif.

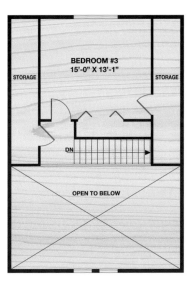

This one-and-a-half story True North design worked out perfectly — both for the size of this treed lot and for the activities of the family. The extensive deck area added considerable living space for these outdoor enthusiasts.

Mackenzie I

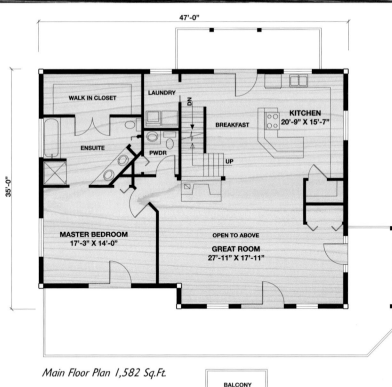

47'-0"

35'-0"

WALK IN CLOSET

LAUNDRY

KITCHEN
20'-9" X 15'-7"

BREAKFAST

ENSUITE

PWDR

DN

UP

MASTER BEDROOM
17'-3" X 14'-0"

OPEN TO ABOVE

GREAT ROOM
27'-11" X 17'-11"

Main Floor Plan 1,582 Sq.Ft.

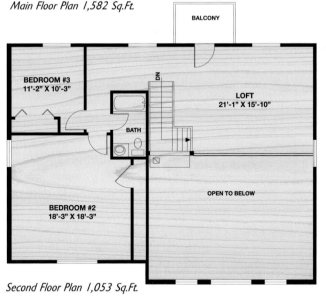

BALCONY

BEDROOM #3
11'-2" X 10'-3"

LOFT
21'-1" X 15'-10"

DN

BATH

BEDROOM #2
18'-3" X 18'-3"

OPEN TO BELOW

Second Floor Plan 1,053 Sq.Ft.

*O*ur guests always comment on the openness of our space. Whether enjoying a meal, playing music or mingling by the fire, our home is perfect for entertaining. Our experience with True North has been great. We especially enjoyed watching the logs go up – it felt like we'd brought the forest into our own home. — C. and P. Ira, True North homeowners, Colorado

Mackenzie
II

The fireplace is the focal point that radiates instant warmth for family gatherings in this expansive great room with twenty-five foot ceilings.

The round log timber truss adds a warm, traditional touch to the private porch overhang.

The all-glass shower highlights the beauty and warmth of the log walls in the five-piece ensuite bathroom.

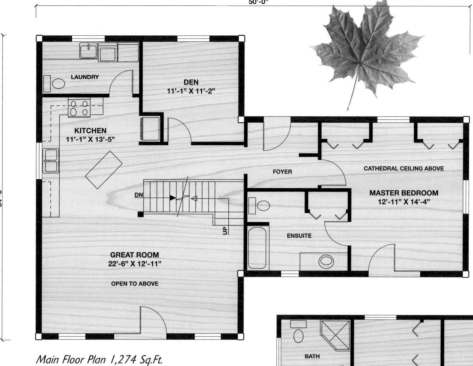

50'-0"

34'-0"

LAUNDRY

DEN
11'-1" X 11'-2"

KITCHEN
11'-1" X 13'-5"

DN

UP

FOYER

CATHEDRAL CEILING ABOVE

MASTER BEDROOM
12'-11" X 14'-4"

ENSUITE

GREAT ROOM
22'-6" X 12'-11"

OPEN TO ABOVE

Main Floor Plan 1,274 Sq.Ft.

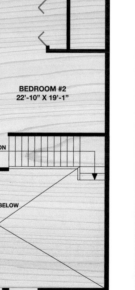
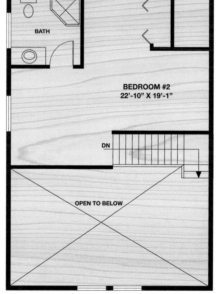

BATH

BEDROOM #2
22'-10" X 19'-1"

DN

OPEN TO BELOW

Second Floor Plan 440 Sq.Ft.

We enjoyed absolutely every aspect of building our True North home. Although we think that everything about our home is just perfect, we find the gazebo to be especially delightful.
— C. Lee and D. Adams
True North homeowners, Minnesota

Mackenzie
III

The Cabot is a quality solution to your desire for an affordable log home that doesn't sacrifice space or features. With its unique rooflines, this compact design attractively depicts each homeowner's design needs and tastes. The Cabot's narrow footprint maximizes floor space, lending itself to narrow or restricted lots, yet is an expansive-looking, attractive home. A double-floor staircase window treatment and two-story window vaulted great room gives this model a spacious feel and a unique character.

THE *Cabot* COLLECTION

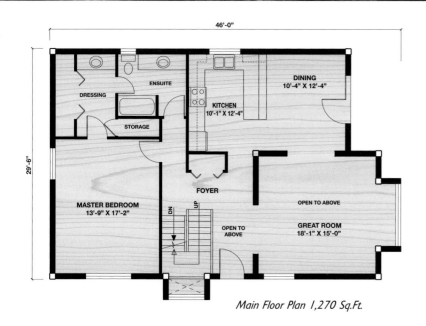

46'-0"

29'-6"

DRESSING

ENSUITE

STORAGE

KITCHEN
10'-1" X 12'-4"

DINING
10'-4" X 12'-4"

FOYER

MASTER BEDROOM
13'-9" X 17'-2"

DN UP

OPEN TO ABOVE

OPEN TO ABOVE

GREAT ROOM
18'-1" X 15'-0"

Main Floor Plan 1,270 Sq.Ft.

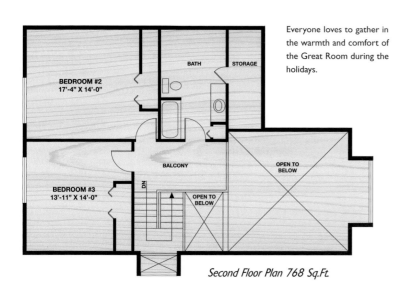

BEDROOM #2
17'-4" X 14'-0"

BATH

STORAGE

BALCONY

OPEN TO BELOW

BEDROOM #3
13'-11" X 14'-0"

DN

OPEN TO BELOW

Second Floor Plan 768 Sq.Ft.

Everyone loves to gather in the warmth and comfort of the Great Room during the holidays.

The natural warmth of this home can be felt even before you enter. The floor to ceiling window treatment lets you enjoy the natural surroundings from almost anywhere in the house. The main floor master bedroom is convenient, while ensuring privacy during family get-togethers.

Cabot
I

46'-0"

29'-6"

LAUNDRY

KITCHEN
10'-11" X 12'-4"

DINING
11'-4" X 12'-4"

BATH

FOYER

DN   UP

OPEN TO
ABOVE

BEDROOM #2
10'-10" X 12'-10"

OPEN TO
ABOVE

LIVING
21'-0" X 15'-0"

Main Floor Plan 1,263 Sq.Ft.

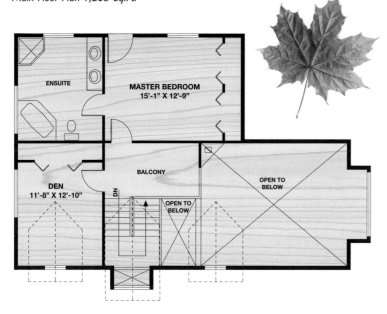

ENSUITE

MASTER BEDROOM
15'-1" X 12'-9"

DEN
11'-8" X 12'-10"

DN

BALCONY

OPEN TO
BELOW

OPEN TO
BELOW

Second Floor Plan 688 Sq.Ft.

Two levels of windows let the light shine in and provide enchanting views of local wildlife.

The custom-designed pool and garden in the backyard creates a welcome retreat.

$\mathcal{W}$ith our True North home, we have been able to create a country place that gives us everything we want for everyday living and for relaxing – we don't need to travel to a cottage to enjoy our leisure time and the outdoors. — J. Sooley and D. Perley, True North homeowners, Carp, Ontario

Cabot
II

Gourmet cooking with a view is pure pleasure within this stately dining area surrounded by a cathedral bay room.

Cathedral ceiling window patterns behind an impressive fireplace with exposed log dovetails provide beautiful design elements of contrasting textures.

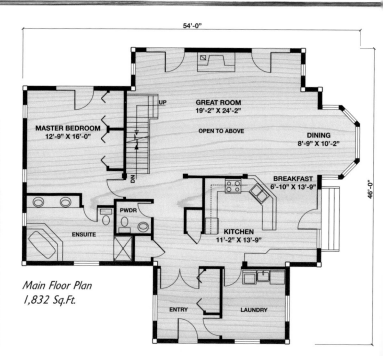

Main Floor Plan
1,832 Sq.Ft.

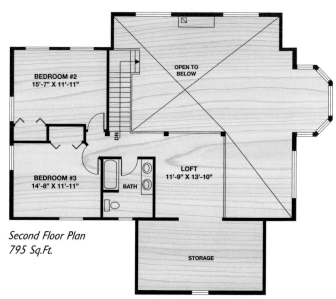

Second Floor Plan
795 Sq.Ft.

The entire experience of the design and build of our True North home surpassed our expectations by far. We love the cozy feel of the logs and the large bay window with views of the creek and forest. — D. and K. Cargill, True North homeowners, Muskoka, Ontario

Cabot III

The True North *Lifestyle...*
Make the most of every moment.

Fun-filled moments...
Enjoy life's fun moments by filling your home with good friends,
spontaneous laughter – and your favourite foods!

Special moments...
Share meaningful moments together
relaxing by the warmth of a fire.

Every True North log home begins with a dream – for a lifestyle that reflects your values and personality, in surroundings that inspire you. A love of nature, an independent spirit and a desire to escape to a natural setting where you can relax with family and friends – this is what the True North lifestyle is all about.

True North Log Homes create extraordinary lifestyle experiences that let you truly enjoy the most precious moments in life.

Quiet moments...
Linger long to savour life's luxurious moments
in your moonlit spa by the lake.

Family moments...
Four season elegance provides endless outdoor adventure
opportunities with children and grandchildren.

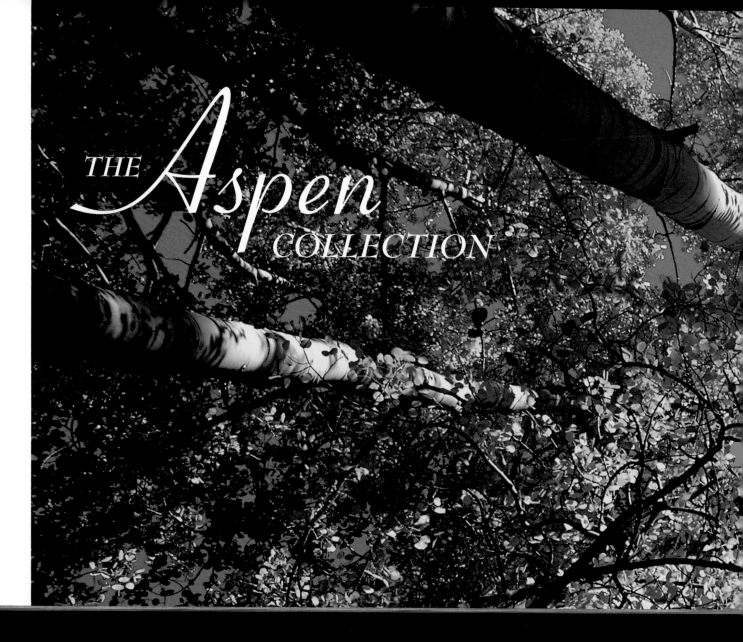

THE *Aspen* COLLECTION

The Aspen provides a wonderful ambience with panoramic views for entertaining indoors and out. This home features a prow gable roof and an abundance of living space enhanced by the floor to ceiling fireplace – the centrepiece of the home. The circular corner areas of the deck create additional living space for the outdoor enthusiast. When the day is done, the hosts can retire to the main-floor master bedroom with cathedral space and gable dormer. The Aspen also offers two large upper bedrooms, including a large loft that overlooks the great room from above.

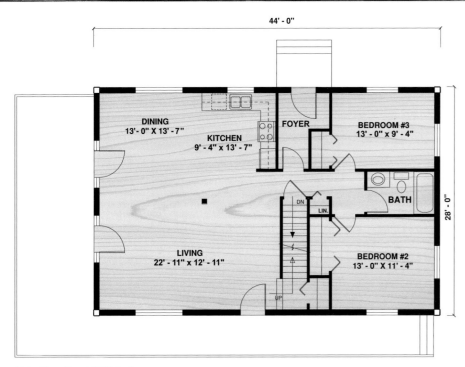

44' - 0"

28' - 0"

DINING
13' - 0" X 13' - 7"

KITCHEN
9' - 4" x 13' - 7"

FOYER

BEDROOM #3
13' - 0" x 9' - 4"

BATH

DN

LIN.

LIVING
22' - 11" x 12' - 11"

BEDROOM #2
13' - 0" X 11' - 4"

UP

Main Floor Plan 1,232 Sq.Ft.

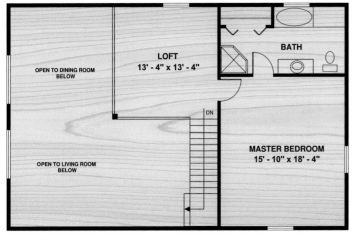

OPEN TO DINING ROOM BELOW

LOFT
13' - 4" x 13' - 4"

BATH

OPEN TO LIVING ROOM BELOW

DN

MASTER BEDROOM
15' - 10" x 18' - 4"

Second Floor Plan 656 Sq.Ft.

The wrap-around counter in this classic kitchen provides a comfy spot for casual dining or for chatting with the chef.

A rocky mountain setting shows off the chalet-style design of this home. The open concept living area with three window walls maximizes viewing opportunities. A loft sitting area extending from the master bedroom area also offers panoramic views of the landscape.

Aspen
I

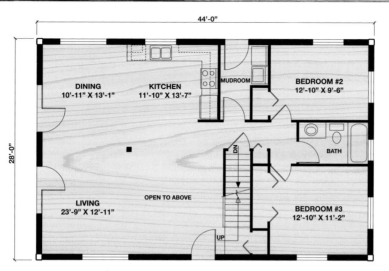

44'-0"

28'-0"

DINING 10'-11" X 13'-1"

KITCHEN 11'-10" X 13'-7"

MUDROOM

BEDROOM #2 12'-10" X 9'-6"

BATH

LIVING 23'-9" X 12'-11"

OPEN TO ABOVE

DN

UP

BEDROOM #3 12'-10" X 11'-2"

Main Floor Plan 1,232 Sq.Ft.

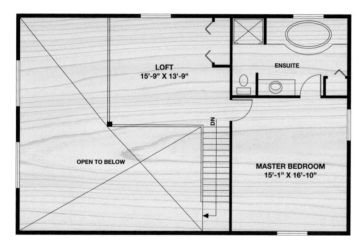

LOFT 15'-9" X 13'-9"

ENSUITE

OPEN TO BELOW

DN

MASTER BEDROOM 15'-1" X 16'-10"

Second Floor Plan 683 Sq.Ft.

The overhanging deck protects the logs and provides additional outdoor living space to kick back and relax, any time day or night, rain or shine.

Although this home is close to a busy highway, the large True North logs insulate the home to provide a quiet oasis.

The large overhang and mix of round and square logs on the deck give our house a modern, yet rustic feel. We love living in a maintenance-free log home that we don't have to work on — that's the advantage of the True North technology. —T. and M. Storlien, True North homeowners, Minnesota

Aspen II

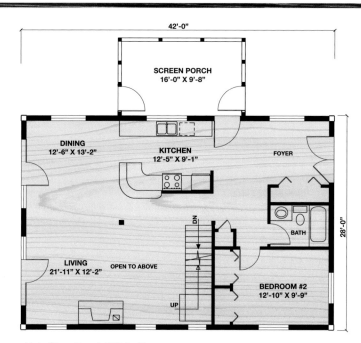

Main Floor Plan 1,176 Sq.Ft.

42'-0"

SCREEN PORCH
16'-0" X 9'-8"

DINING
12'-6" X 13'-2"

KITCHEN
12'-5" X 9'-1"

FOYER

BATH

LIVING
21'-11" X 12'-2"

OPEN TO ABOVE

BEDROOM #2
12'-10" X 9'-9"

UP

28'-0"

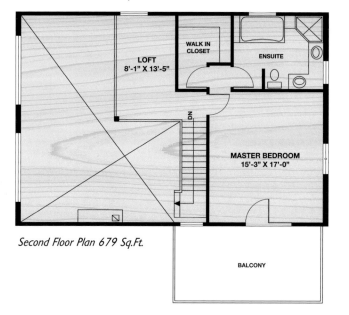

Second Floor Plan 679 Sq.Ft.

WALK IN CLOSET

ENSUITE

LOFT
8'-1" X 13'-5"

DN

MASTER BEDROOM
15'-3" X 17'-0"

BALCONY

An open concept dining and great room area, with soaring cathedral ceilings, offer views of the lake, forest and skies from anywhere in the home.

A spectacular stone fireplace provides a centerpiece for comfort and relaxation after a long work week.

I work twelve-to fifteen-hour days and could not keep up the pace without coming home to decompress. Every night I look at the logs and the fireplace and think, wow — what did I do to deserve this? It's like being on holidays every weekend! The True North product is truly exceptional. — C. Turgeon, True North homeowner, Ottawa, Ontario

Aspen III

SUNROOM
13'-0" X 11'-3"

DINING
13'-0" X 13'-8"

KITCHEN
13'8" X 11'8"

BEDROOM #2
12'-10" X 9'-8"

OPEN TO ABOVE

BATH

DN

LIVING
25'-6" X 12'-10"

BEDROOM #3
12'-8" X 11'4"

UP

46'-0"

28'-0"

Main Floor Plan 1,278 Sq.Ft.
Sunroom 155 Sq.Ft.

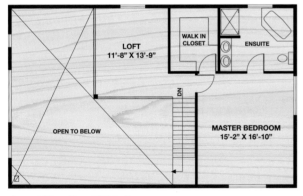

LOFT
11'-8" X 13'-9"

WALK IN
CLOSET

ENSUITE

DN

OPEN TO BELOW

MASTER BEDROOM
15'-2" X 16'-10"

Second Floor Plan 687 Sq.Ft.

The unique sunroom addition adds interest to the Aspen profile while providing the perfect spot to catch up on reading or do a bit of bird-watching.

*W*e are extremely happy with our lifestyle here. Every morning we have coffee in the sunroom with a view of the lake and we also especially enjoy the warm cozy loft. Our True North dealer was outstanding throughout the entire building process. — L. and R. Culbertson, True North homeowners, Minnesota

Aspen IV

The cozy bedroom beckons children to dream
about their next fishing trip with granddad.

Sink into a deep leather sofa or chair with a beverage in
the great room to talk about the latest catch.

The gleaming black granite island-top provides a contrast
to the warmth of the surrounding wood in the kitchen.

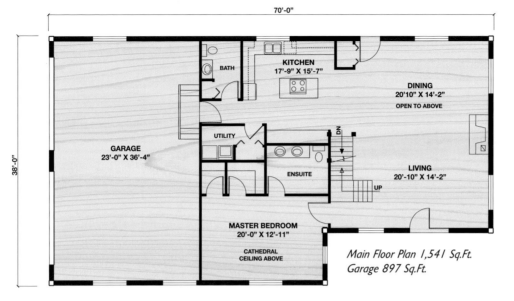

70'-0"

38'-0"

GARAGE
23'-0" X 36'-4"

BATH

KITCHEN
17'-9" X 15'-7"

DINING
20'10" X 14'-2"
OPEN TO ABOVE

UTILITY

ENSUITE

DN

LIVING
20'-10" X 14'-2"

UP

MASTER BEDROOM
20'-0" X 12'-11"

CATHEDRAL
CEILING ABOVE

Main Floor Plan 1,541 Sq.Ft.
Garage 897 Sq.Ft.

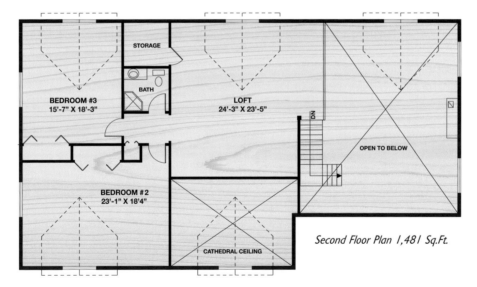

STORAGE

BATH

BEDROOM #3
15'-7" X 18'-3"

LOFT
24'-3" X 23'-5"

DN

OPEN TO BELOW

BEDROOM #2
23'-1" X 18'4"

CATHEDRAL CEILING

Second Floor Plan 1,481 Sq.Ft.

The kitchen island compliments the multi-hued stone used for the fireplace, providing a distinctive contrast to the beauty of the floor and beams.

We wanted the look and feel of a wilderness lodge, and as you can see we got it. The wrap-around deck significantly adds to the appearance of our log home - it was like adding a bowtie to a tuxedo! — M. & S. Mattson, True North homeowners, Minnesota

Aspen V

Ultra-comfy furniture invites visitors to lounge in the centre of the classic great room, surrounded by light and the warmth from the stone fireplace that rises to the peak of the vaulted ceiling.

The serenity and simplicity of the gabled ceiling roof design in the upstairs bedroom makes it so easy to drift off into a deep slumber.

The full deck is extended to create an enchanting circular space to relax after dinner.

All you need is your favourite book to enjoy the lakeside deck.

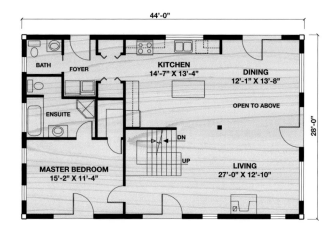

44'-0"

BATH FOYER KITCHEN 14'-7" X 13'-4" DINING 12'-1" X 13'-8"

ENSUITE

OPEN TO ABOVE

DN UP

MASTER BEDROOM 15'-2" X 11'-4" LIVING 27'-0" X 12'-10"

28'-0"

Main Floor Plan 1,230 Sq.Ft.

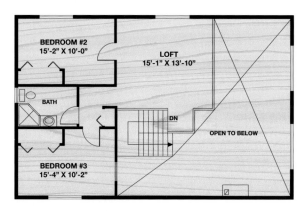

BEDROOM #2 15'-2" X 10'-0" LOFT 15'-1" X 13'-10"

BATH

DN

OPEN TO BELOW

BEDROOM #3 15'-4" X 10'-2"

Second Floor Plan 680 Sq.Ft.

A kitchen island, composed of handpicked granite from South Africa, sets the stage for a casual lunch. Modern stainless steel counters and a mix of antique black and alder wood cabinetry provide a stunning contrast to the log beams.

*E*very time we walk into our house, we smell the wood and immediately feel cozy and comfortable. We chose True North for the open design style and product quality. We were very impressed to learn about the patents and technology of True North. We couldn't be happier with our home.
— B. and S. Silcox, True North homeowners, Minnesota

Aspen VI

The wall-to-wall windows and doors are custom-designed by the owner to ensure lake views from both the great room and loft.

The owner scored a home run when he found 100-year-old reclaimed
lumber from the Milwaukee County Baseball Stadium
to use for the hardwood flooring.

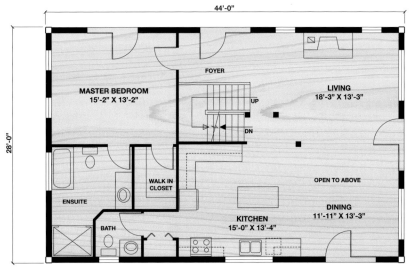

Main Floor Plan 1,232 Sq.Ft.

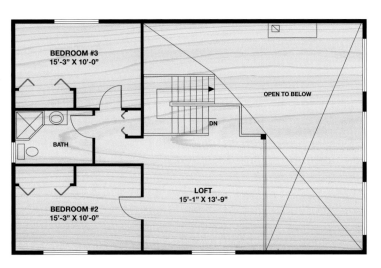

Second Floor Plan 692 Sq.Ft.

Distinctive furnishings, like this
handcrafted log bed, complement
the design of the home.

$\mathcal{T}$rue North provided an outstanding contractor, who helped us turn our
vacation home into reality. Our custom-designed firepit is a favourite spot
for sharing impromptu sing-a-longs, stories and laughter.

— K. and A. Bares,
True North homeowners, Minnesota

Aspen
VII

The unique log staircase beckons guests to a quiet bedroom retreat.

Vaulted ceilings and windows dominate the open living area allowing panoramic views from sunrise to sunset.

Large exposed ceiling beams combined with antique black furniture highlight this gourmet kitchen.

Your home is the ultimate expression of you. True North can work with you to design a unique, one-of-a-kind home that truly reflects your personality and tastes. The homes featured in this section display the ingenuity of our design team, coupled with the homeowners' desires and dreams — from a Southwest-inspired ranch, to a scenic mountain retreat, to the simple rustic elegance of a home in the forest. Let your imagination run wild… as we look forward to the adventure of helping you realize your log home dream.

THE *Custom* COLLECTION

A simple and elegant entry welcomes visitors into the central great room with cathedral ceilings and expansive windows.

Main Floor Plan 3,090 Sq.Ft.

83' - 0"

45' - 0"

MASTER BEDROOM
27' - 4" X 18' - 3"

GREAT ROOM
26' - 1" X 31' - 3"

DINING ROOM
27' - 6" X 16' - 0"

CATHEDRAL CEILING ABOVE

HALF WALL

KITCHEN
27' - 6" X 11' - 2"

ENSUITE

DN

OFFICE
17' - 8" X 12' - 0"

STOR.

PANTRY

BATH

LAUNDRY

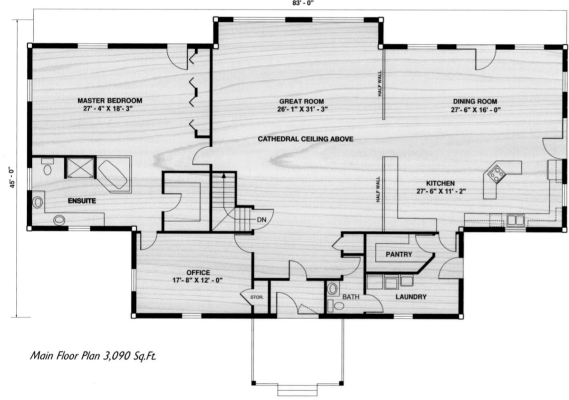

This custom bungalow provides everything you need for relaxing, working or entertaining friends. At the end of the day, homeowners look forward to the large master bedroom with the luxurious ensuite spa!

Custom *Castlerock*

Chairs with cowboy-themed tapestry and a hanging replica antler light, capture the essence of this El Dorado ranch house.

The orthopedic-friendly stairs have been specially designed to minimize wear and tear on knees.

GREAT ROOM 20'-5" X 32'-0"

DINING 16'-0" X 12'-9"

OPEN TO ABOVE

MASTER BEDROOM 15'-9" X 21'-1"

WALK IN CLOSET

SUNROOM 11'-7" X 20'-10"

ENSUITE

KITCHEN 15'-8" X 16'-0"

PANTRY

UP DN

ENSUITE

LAUNDRY

POWDER

FOYER

GUEST 17'-10" X 17'-11"

WALK IN CLOSET

41'-0"

Main Floor Plan 3,379 Sq.Ft. ————— 78'-0"

GUEST 15'-7" X 15'7"

OPEN TO BELOW

BEDROOM #2 15'-7" X 13'-1"

STORAGE

STORAGE

BATH

WALK IN CLOSET

DN

BATH

LOFT 52'-2" X 13'-3"

Second Floor Plan 1,605 Sq.Ft.

Custom *El Dorado*

The rolling hills of Arkansas can be seen from picturesque windows framed by the large window bumpout feature, while Southwest Indian artifacts add a sense of history.

This luxury Ozark-style ranch home features dormer windows, metal roof, luxurious wrap-around porches and full walk-out basement.

A chef's dream, this kitchen space features a six-burner stovetop built into the granite-top island and visible storage area to select your favourite jar of homemade pickles, jam or jelly.

A southwest design theme enhances this oversize great room, including a unique ladder to the loft, a replica of those once used by New Mexico natives to access underground dwellings.

52'-0"

42'-0"

KITCHEN
15'-1" X 16'-0"

DINING
12'-5" X 24'-0"

MUDROOM

PREPARATION ROOM

POWDER

DN

LIVING
17'-4" X 17'-6"

FOYER

UP

GREAT ROOM
17'-10" X 16'-5"

Main Floor Plan 1,679 Sq.Ft.

BATH

BEDROOM #3
24'-0" X 10'-11"

BALCONY

ENSUITE

LAUNDRY

WALK IN CLOSET

DN

MASTER BEDROOM
17'-4" X 17'-6"

LIBRARY
15'-3" X 18'-8"

BATH

BEDROOM #2
17'-3" X 16'-6"

Second Floor Plan 1,670 Sq.Ft.

Stone, wood and multi-coloured stained glass highlight the varied tones and textures in the hallway. Guests are welcomed with a cup of tea or coffee simmering on the antique stove.

The two story dovetails are the focal point of this awe inspiring home.

The fireplace, window mouldings and wicker furniture accentuate the natural beauty and varied tones of the surrounding wood.

We love the look and feel of our True North home. We were looking for simple, rustic beauty and this is what we have achieved. We love the windows, porches and open concept. We've added a warm Victorian feel with old-fashioned style appliances and a wood stove. — L. and G. Landry, True North homeowners, Guelph, Ontario

Custom **Timberland**

Earth tones in this "dream kitchen" reflect the outside. Cherry wood cabinets, forest green trim and pine floors offset the brilliant white hues of Italian porcelain on the island and counter tops.

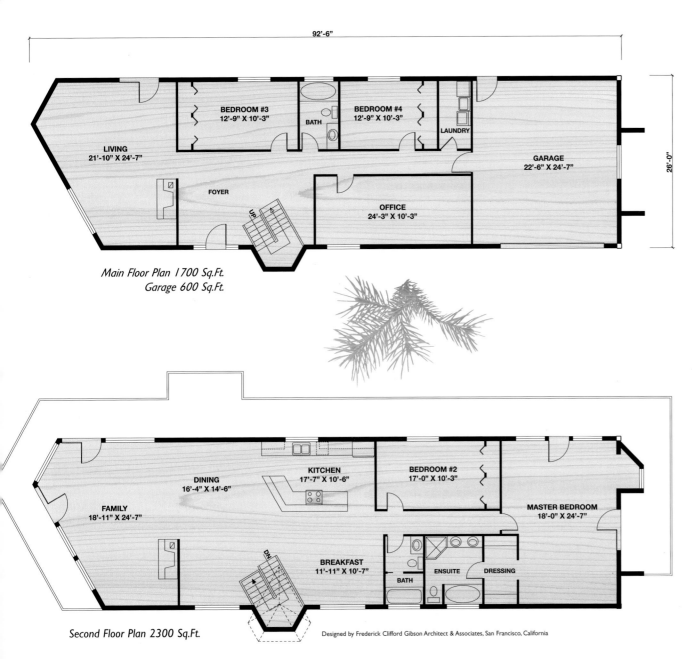

92'-6"

26'-0"

BEDROOM #3
12'-9" X 10'-3"

BATH

BEDROOM #4
12'-9" X 10'-3"

LAUNDRY

LIVING
21'-10" X 24'-7"

GARAGE
22'-6" X 24'-7"

FOYER

UP

OFFICE
24'-3" X 10'-3"

Main Floor Plan 1700 Sq.Ft.
Garage 600 Sq.Ft.

DINING
16'-4" X 14'-6"

KITCHEN
17'-7" X 10'-6"

BEDROOM #2
17'-0" X 10'-3"

FAMILY
18'-11" X 24'-7"

MASTER BEDROOM
18'-0" X 24'-7"

DN

BREAKFAST
11'-11" X 10'-7"

BATH

ENSUITE

DRESSING

Second Floor Plan 2300 Sq.Ft.

Designed by Frederick Clifford Gibson Architect & Associates, San Francisco, California

*A*s nature-lovers, our home is perfect. It's as if we're living in the outdoors, but in a beautiful, comfortable space. Every morning we see the mountain views before we even get up and then realize how lucky we are. We were extremely pleased with how True North worked with our one-of-a-kind design.
— D. and A. Chapin,
True North homeowners, Colorado

Custom
Keystone

The design of the open arched entry into the spa,
painted in golden hues, is Mexican inspired.

This home is ideal for entertaining. Guests are surrounded by mountain
views and a fireplace from wherever they choose to lounge or dine.

Antique furnishings surround the dramatic, two-storey fireplace,
adding a touch of warmth to a contemporary home.

The Mexican-style décor in the master bedroom features a tiva-styled fireplace and a window design that creates dramatic lighting with a dazzling mix of light and shadows from the sun and moonlight.

U-shaped stairs leading to an upper living space with a wrapping fitted deck is just one of many unique features found in this custom-designed home.

THE Lafontaine COLLECTION

The Lafontaine is a well-planned bungalow/ranch style home that is designed to compliment your lifestyle. The design options are only limited by your imagination. The Lafontaine features a master bedroom and ensuite at one end of the home and guest bedrooms at the opposite end, giving homeowners and their guests maximum privacy. The sunroom off the master bedroom can also be used as a nursery, library or office. Bay windows in the master bedroom and breakfast nook enhance the main entrance, while adding light and warmth to this striking home.

Main Floor Plan

77'-0"

50'-0"

BATH

CATHEDRAL CEILING

BEDROOM #2
14'-2" X 12'-4"

WALK IN CLOSET

LAUNDRY

BATH

DN — UP

HOT TUB

SPA
19'-10" X 15'-9"

SWIM POOL

BEDROOM #1
12'-4" X 15'-9"

DINING
27'-1" X 13'-2"

OPEN TO ABOVE

GREAT ROOM
27'-1" X 23'-4"

CATHEDRAL CEILING

KITCHEN
14'-7" X 23'-8"

BATH

MUD ROOM

OFFICE
14'-7" X 16'-10"

Main Floor Plan 3,385 Sq.Ft.

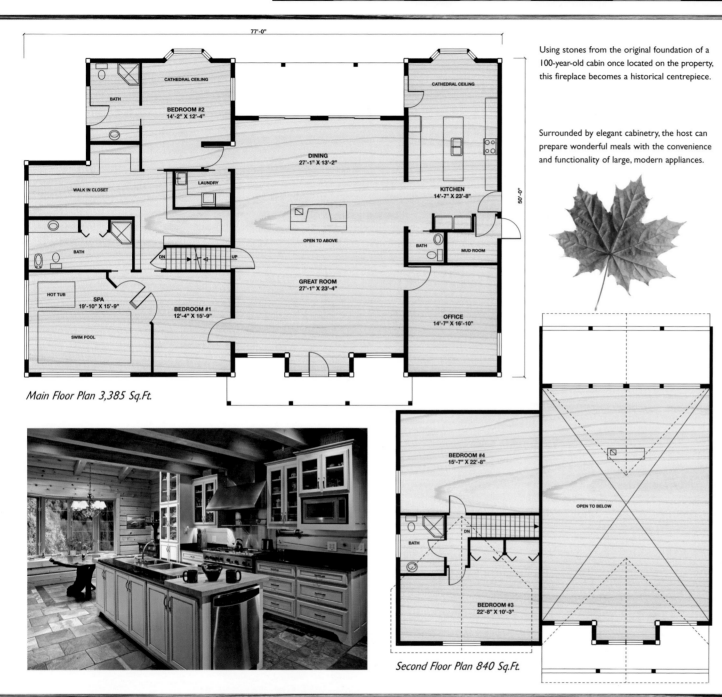

BEDROOM #4
15'-7" X 22'-8"

OPEN TO BELOW

BATH

DN

BEDROOM #3
22'-8" X 10'-3"

Second Floor Plan 840 Sq.Ft.

Using stones from the original foundation of a 100-year-old cabin once located on the property, this fireplace becomes a historical centrepiece.

Surrounded by elegant cabinetry, the host can prepare wonderful meals with the convenience and functionality of large, modern appliances.

*W*e designed every inch of our home and now enjoy a spacious house full of light and warmth. I've always wanted a 'tree house' and now we have it — True North provided the quality to help us fulfill our dream. — M. and P. Davis, True North homeowners, Georgia

Lafontaine
I

This majestic stone fireplace beckons friends to share the warmth together in the dining room, or to relax before a roaring fire in the living room.

With forest views, this soothing spa welcomes friends to relax in the pool or hot tub

Step into the grand foyer to view the colours of the variegated palette from the natural slate flooring that is found throughout the home. This exotic flooring comes from Kashmir and is no-maintenance and worry-free.

The energy of the forest filters through bay windows and skylights to create a calming effect for reading, sleeping or just relaxing.

Sq. Ft.	2,146	Plan #	86101	Bedrooms	Three	Baths	Two

65'-6"
37'-6"
LIVING
19'-5" X 19'-6"
CATHEDRAL CEILING
SUN ROOM
15'-3" X 8'-0"
BATH
LAUNDRY
BEDROOM #3
11'-0" X 11'-2"
ENSUITE
WALK IN CLOSET
FOYER
DINING
13'-10" X 11'-9"
KITCHEN
13'-3" X 11'-8"
BEDROOM #2
14'-6" X 10'-9"
MASTER BEDROOM
12'-6" X 20'-6"
BREAKFAST NOOK
12'-6" X 13'-3"

Main Floor Plan 2,146 Sq.Ft.

The open living room is a comfy paradise for capturing the constant, changing scenes of Mother Nature.

This family log home is perfectly suited to a landscaped lot, while letting you enjoy being "in the woods." The great room with cathedral ceilings and expansive windows continues to be a favourite place for relaxing and entertaining guests.

Lafontaine II

84'-6"

41'-6"

SUNROOM
13'-0" X 7'-8"

KITCHEN
15'-10" X 15'-4"

LIVING
19'-1" X 21'-4"

CATHEDRAL CEILING

SCREENED PORCH
14'-6" X 14'-5"

MASTER BEDROOM
17'-9" X 15'-4"

DINING
19'-7" X 11'-0"

BATH

OFFICE
10'-8" X 10'-3"

FOYER

GARAGE
14'-6" X 18'-10"

LAUNDRY

DN

SAUNA

BEDROOM #2
14'-6" X 10'-7"

ENSUITE

Main Floor Plan 2,276 Sq.Ft.   Garage 316 Sq.Ft.   Screened Porch 210 Sq.Ft.

Majestic dovetails frame this dream kitchen with cranberry appliances and hunter green cabinets. Whether seated at the island or preparing a meal, there is always a picturesque view of the river.

This is a magical place, offering cozy Canadian comfort, combined with extreme luxury. It is heartwarming to know that dreams really can come true. "My Indian River Dream Bed and Breakfast guests often ask if I would build another True North Log Home and to that I reply, In a minute!"
— M. Campbell, owner, Indian River Dream, Bed, Breakfast and Spa, Muskoka, Ontario

Lafontaine III

Decked out for the holidays, the great room becomes a magical setting for an evening of Christmas carols.

This home reflects the true spirit of the region with a spectacular, full-length deck, rear screen porch and sunroom where guests can enjoy the stunning views.

Customers keep returning to this distinguished log bed and breakfast home for the comfort, luxury and hospitality.

Whether for everyday living or for use as a seasonal getaway, True North's cabin designs can provide exactly what you are looking for to escape your fast-paced lifestyle – a perfect retirement home, the best Bunkie in the world or your favourite place for a weekend away.

Log and timber construction can be extremely well-suited to commercial and non-residential applications, especially in the tourism sector. Recreational property owners experience a huge return on investment due to the increased traffic and appeal created by the rustic charm and quality construction of a True North product.

Cabins/Commercial
COLLECTION

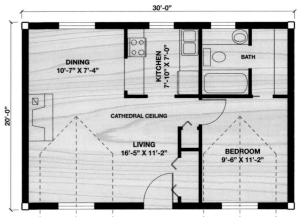

Main Floor Plan 600 Sq.Ft.

With a large open kitchen area, a well-proportioned master bedroom and space for extra bedrooms in the optional loft, this cabin-style home is well suited as a starter home or weekend retreat.

This is the perfect "cabin in the woods" that you've always dreamed of! The attic space can be turned into a sleeping loft to be enjoyed by friends during those winter cross-country ski treks.

Killarney
I

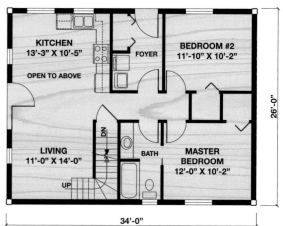

Main Floor Plan 884 Sq.Ft.

KITCHEN 13'-3" X 10'-5"

OPEN TO ABOVE

FOYER

BEDROOM #2 11'-10" X 10'-2"

LIVING 11'-0" X 14'-0"

DN

BATH

MASTER BEDROOM 12'-0" X 10'-2"

UP

34'-0"

26'-0"

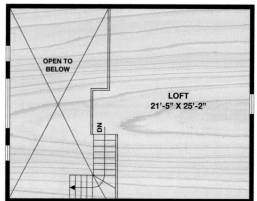

Second Floor Plan 528 Sq.Ft.

OPEN TO BELOW

LOFT 21'-5" X 25'-2"

DN

The cozy rooms in this home, including a lovely upstairs loft, are surrounded by a hand crafted log wrap-around deck.

*O*ur home is so warm and relaxing – when we walk inside, we immediately feel the calming effect of the natural logs. We also love being able to enjoy the forest from our walkout deck. I recommend True North to all my friends because of the excellent quality of the product. — R. and J. Dickie, True North homeowners, Minnesota

Killarney II

Alterations to the floor plan can be made to accommodate a kitchen or other living arrangements.

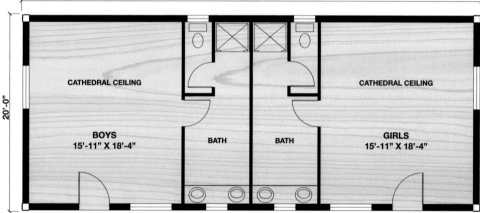

48'-0"

20'-0"

CATHEDRAL CEILING

CATHEDRAL CEILING

BOYS
15'-11" X 18'-4"

BATH

BATH

GIRLS
15'-11" X 18'-4"

Main Floor Plan 960 Sq.Ft.

*O*ur "Bunkie" was specially designed for the kids, with two identical, separate units to provide a "his" and "hers" space, with the boys on one side, and the girls the other. Each separate side has it's own entrance and bath. —True North homeowner, Montebello, Quebec

Killarney III

64'-0"

28'-0"

UP

UP

BATH

BATH BATH

BATH

SUITE #1
15'-4" X 26'-6"

SUITE #2
14'-11" X 26'-6"

SUITE #3
14'-11" X 26'-6"

SUITE #4
15'-4" X 26'-6"

Main Floor Plan 1,784 Sq.Ft.

BATH

BATH BATH

BATH

SUITE #5
15'-4" X 26'-6"

SUITE #6
14'-11" X 26'-6"

SUITE #7
14'-11" X 26'-6"

SUITE #8
15'-4" X 26'-6"

DN

DN

Second Floor Plan 1,784 Sq.Ft.

*W*e constantly receive positive customer feedback on how nice and cozy our rooms feel, and how different we are from a typical hotel. The logs really enhance the warmth and tranquility of our accommodations. — Owner, Sunset Inn on the Park, Lake Nipissing, North Bay, Ontario

Commercial

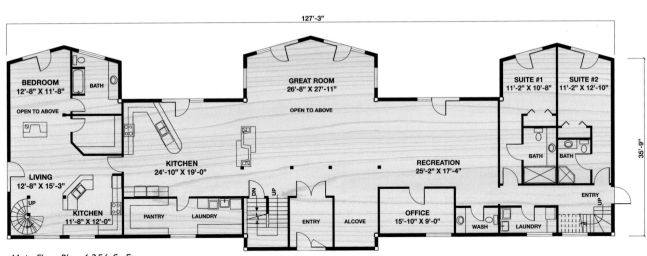

127'-3"

BEDROOM 12'-8" X 11'-8"

BATH

OPEN TO ABOVE

GREAT ROOM 26'-8" X 27'-11"

OPEN TO ABOVE

SUITE #1 11'-2" X 10'-8"

SUITE #2 11'-2" X 12'-10"

LIVING 12'-8" X 15'-3"

KITCHEN 24'-10" X 19'-0"

RECREATION 25'-2" X 17'-4"

BATH

BATH

35'-9"

UP

KITCHEN 11'-8" X 12'-0"

PANTRY

LAUNDRY

DN

UP

ENTRY

ALCOVE

OFFICE 15'-10" X 9'-0"

WASH

LAUNDRY

ENTRY

UP

Main Floor Plan 4,356 Sq.Ft.

You're never too far from nature in this guest room where you can fall asleep under the Alaskan sky.

The Great Room is a perfect setting for sharing the day's fishing adventures with friends.

OPEN TO BELOW

BALCONY

OPEN TO BELOW

BALCONY

SUITE #6 22'-8" X 15'-5"

LOFT 12'-5" X 34'-6"

SUITE #3 24'-7" X 19'-2"

SUITE #4 11'-10" X 9'-9"

SUITE #5 11'-10" X 9'-9"

BATH

DN

BATH

BATH

STORAGE

DN

BATH

BATH

GAMES 19'-3" X 16'-3"

STORAGE

DN

Second Floor Plan 3,171 Sq.Ft.

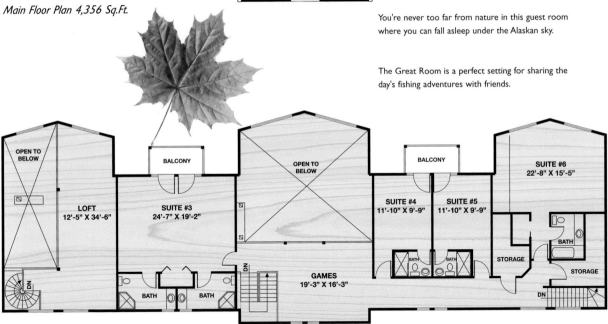

$\mathcal{T}$he moment guests enter our home, they are awestruck by the beauty and warmth. True North helped us create a home that is beyond our wildest dreams and a fishing lodge that has become a memorable retreat for the many outdoor enthusiasts that visit us. — S. and J. Hamilton, True North homeowners, Alaska.

Commercial

What's *Included*

6

9

6a *(optional)*

6

4a *(optional)*

4

12 *(optional)*

11 *(optional)*

7

10 *(optional)*

4c *(optional)*

1

3

5

2

8

4b *(optional)*

4

Log Home Shell Package, Building Specifications

1) LOGWALL PACKAGE:

All custom milled, double tongue and groove with exclusive patented dovetail or saddlenotch corner, Northeastern white pine timbers, 6" x 12", 8" x 12" or 10" x 12" logs. (12" x 12" logs available upon special request) Western red cedar is also available.

2) LOG WALL ACCESSORIES:

SILL GASKET: Closed cell waterproof foam gasket for foundation perimeter.
SILL PLATE: 2" x 6", 8" or 10" cedar sill plate for foundation perimeter.
TOP LOG PLATES: 2" x 6" Spruce top log plates for wall to ceiling connection.
SILL POLY: Black sill membrane for air/vapour barrier continuity at ceilings and openings.
FLASHING: Prepainted 28-gauge sill flashing for exterior sill plate perimeter.
THRU-BOLTS: Spring-loaded thru-bolts for 6"x12" exterior log walls as required.
NEW LOG LOCK: For exterior log walls 8"x12", 10"x12", 12"x12" (6"x12" optional)
LOG JOINERY: Patented KeyLocks, Butt Splines and KeySplines, Custom-cut Corner, Butt Spline and KeySpline foam pad seals.
LOG JOINT SEAL: Six Seal System on 8"x12", 10"x12", 12"x12" logs (4 foams, 2 butyl tapes) double tongue and groove.
3 Seal System on 6"x12" logs (1 foam, 2 butyl tapes) double tongue & groove.
STEEL ALIGNMENT: High strength steel reinforcement bars for exterior log wall openings.

3) STAIN PACKAGE: (factory applied)

Climate controlled, factory applied primer coat to all logs at time of manufacture.

Site STAIN PACKAGE : (optional) (customer applied)

Exterior / interior stain coat and topcoat applied to logs and exterior pine areas on site.

4) WINDOW/ EXTERIOR DOOR PACKAGE:

Wood thermal pane windows and insulated steel partially glazed entrance doors, Exterior trims and jamb extensions. **4a.** True North custom camber top trims (optional) **4b.** Coloured aluminum clad windows (optional) **4c.** Solid wood interior doors (optional)

5) FIRST & SECOND FLOOR FRAMING SYSTEM:

Jack or wood posts, built-up wood beams, dimensional lumber floor joists, joist hangers, cross bridging, spruce plywood tongue and groove sub-floor and sub-floor adhesive.

6) ROOF SYSTEM:

Pre-engineered and custom-designed for maximum loading with cantilevered overhangs to allow for more ventilation and insulation space. All required trusses, dimensional lumber framing, ladder framing, dormer framing, bracing, hangers, 1/2" spruce plywood sheathing, 15-lb felt paper, 1x 8 V-groove pine soffit material, sub-fascia and 1x 8 pine fascia material. **6a.** Gable and dormer lookouts (optional)

7) GABLE END FRAMING SYSTEM:

2" x 6" spruce rough framing, 7/16" oriented strand board sheathing, strapping, moisture barrier, and 1 x 8 pine rustic channel siding.

8) INTERIOR STUDWALL FRAMING:

2" x 4" and 2" x 6" SPF interior partition wall framing for first and second floors. All steel slide assemblies for framed wall to log wall connections and spikes for interior wall alignment.

9) ASPHALT SHINGLE ROOF SYSTEM:

25 year asphalt shingles, ice and water shield, valley flashing, endwall flashing, step flashing, roof vents, soffit vents, and starter strip. Steel & cedar roofing optional.

10) BEAMS AND FLOORING OPTIONS:

Heavy timber beams 2"x 8" tongue & groove pine flooring, and acoustical caulking.

11) HEAVY TIMBER TRUSS OPTIONS:

Timber truss gable and door treatments. Heavy timber truss porch systems. Available in square timber or handcrafted round logs.

12) LOG SIDING OPTIONS:

2"x12" white pine log siding available in all profiles.

The Finest Wood in North America

The most valuable soft wood in North America goes into every True North log home. Grown in the forests of Northern Ontario and Quebec, this winter-cut, slow growth Northeastern white pine tree is carefully chosen by True North for the log wall system of your home. Only the durable heartwood of the log is used, making the log extremely dimensionally stable. The sapwood section, or soft layers between the heartwood and the bark is eliminated in the squaring process. This assures that settlement of the logs will be minimal – not exceeding one inch in an eight-foot wall height. Western red cedar is also available upon request.

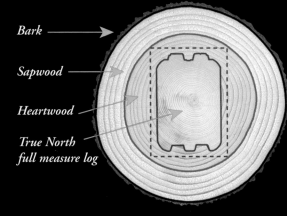

Bark →

Sapwood →

Heartwood →

True North full measure log →

12"
Full Measure

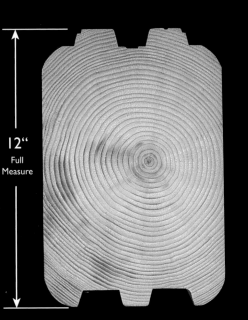

Round Groove

"V" Groove

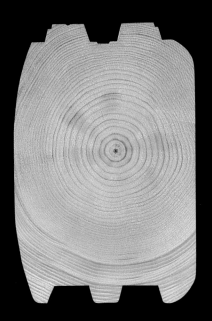

Outside "D"

Double "D"

Tear Drop

FULL-SIZE LOGS MEAN GREATER VALUE.

True North uses only full dimensional logs. This means, for example, the 8" x 12" log actually measures 8" x 12", as opposed to the 7 1/4" x 11 1/4" logs used by others in the industry. True North's use of full-size logs translates into greater insulative value. The bottom line is that the larger the logs, the more thermal mass, which equals more energy efficiency!

A wide variety of log shapes and corner styles are offered by True North. The choices cover the entire spectrum of North American log dwellings and design choices, from square to round shapes, from dovetail to saddlenotch corners and from smooth to rough faces.

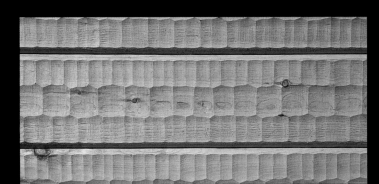

Explore the many unique options offered by True North. The "Adzed" log face finish is gaining great popularity in North America.

The *Patented*
Butt Spline Assembly

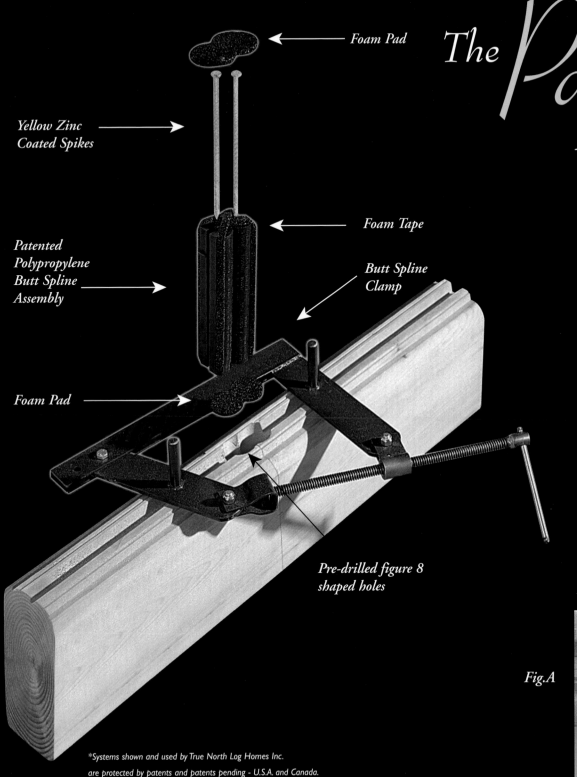

Foam Pad

Yellow Zinc
Coated Spikes

Foam Tape

Patented
Polypropylene
Butt Spline
Assembly

Butt Spline
Clamp

Foam Pad

Pre-drilled figure 8
shaped holes

*Systems shown and used by True North Log Homes Inc.
are protected by patents and patents pending - U.S.A. and Canada.*

A) Two holes are drilled in the end of each log to create a figure 8 shape as they butt together in a wall assembly.

B) A custom made-butt spline clamp is inserted into pre-drilled clamping holes and pressure is applied to draw the joint together.

C) An asphalt-impregnated figure 8 foam pad is installed in the bottom of the figure 8 shaped holes.

D) A two-piece patented polypropylene butt spline assembly is wrapped with asphalt foam tape and then dropped into the figure 8 shaped holes.

E) Two 10 inch common spikes are driven into the two piece butt spline assembly, wedging it apart, thus tightening the joint. This procedure is similar to attaching an axe to an axe handle with a wedge.

F) Another asphalt-impregnated figure 8 foam pad is installed on top of the butt spline assembly.

G) Finally the butt spline clamp is removed.

TRUE NORTH'S SECRET...

The green arrows in *Fig. A* demonstrate the natural shrinkage in the width of the log. The log squeezes on the radius of the butt spline assembly. At the same time, shown with blue arrows, the log shrinks longitudinally, pulling on the butt spline assembly, making the joint progressively tighter over time.

Patented Polypropylene Butt Spline Assembly Fully Installed

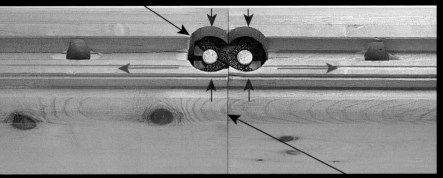

Fig.A

No Air Infiltration Through The Joint

The *Six Seal*
Patented Tongue and Groove System

"The best just keeps getting better! I've built quite a few of these homes, and the new Six Seal System is very impressive. Better thermal performance equals a better investment for the customer. It's a pleasure to work with True North, where continuous product improvements really mean something".

– Doug Mason Construction, True North builder, homeowner

True North's new Six Seal system is an example of the kind of research and technology that makes True North the #1 choice among log homebuyers today.

FURTHER IMPROVING THE TRUE NORTH LOG JOINERY SYSTEM

The newly released Six Seal tongue and groove system is a recent innovation for True North Log Homes and available on our 8"x12", 10"x12" and 12"x12" logs. The True North tongue and groove technology is designed with six channels to accommodate the butyl rubber tape sealant and the foam gasket tape. The outside channels are angled to accommodate the butyl tape. During construction, this unique angle prevents the butyl tape from falling off while setting the log above and actually increases the seal from 1/4" to 3/8" as we are utilizing the diagonal of the butyl tape instead of the width from side to side. This increases performance without the extra cost of a 3/8" seal. The channels also prevent the sealant from being completely flattened out by the upper log, so when movement occurs in the logs, a sufficient amount of sealant is still able to flex. The remaining four channels are designed to accommodate the foam tapes. The foam tape provides insulation value and when compressed 50% it becomes waterproof.

The thermal performance can be compared to a thermal pane window: if the six seals represent six panes of glass, the trapped air space between the glass will act as an insulator. Each section of dead air space between the tongue and groove seals reacts in the same way thereby improving thermal performance.

The Six Seal tongue and groove system enhances thermal performance and significantly improves the sealing capabilities of the tongue and groove joints between the logs.

The original Three Seal tongue and groove system, as shown to the right, is used with our 6"x12" log construction.

THREE SEAL SYSTEM

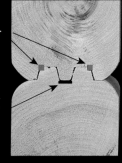

Butyl Rubber
Tape Sealant

Foam Gasket
Tape

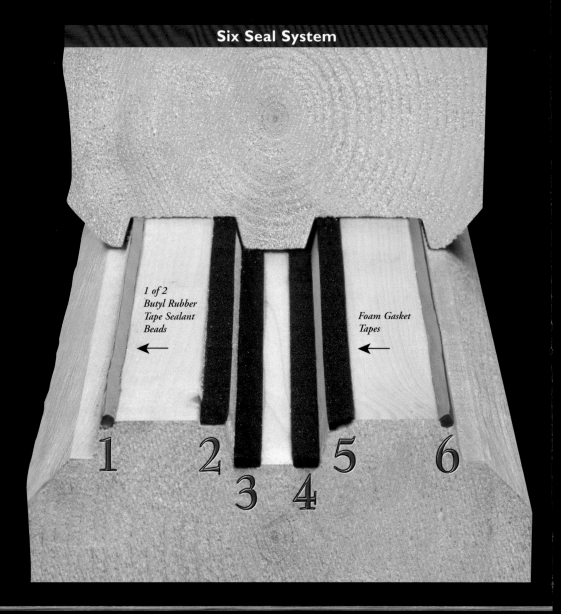

Six Seal System

1 of 2
Butyl Rubber
Tape Sealant
Beads
←

Foam Gasket
Tapes
←

1 2 3 4 5 6

TRUE NORTH LOG CORNERS

The strength of any building is the corner. The cornerstone, as they say, of a log home is even more important. The major problem is log home corner joinery separation. True North has resolved this problem by incorporating their patented Keylock Air Seal Corner®. into every True North home!

True North applies only the most advanced corner systems and technologies into your log home. These systems include the dovetail, saddlenotch and post corners, unlike other builders who opt for the easier to produce "butt and pass" system, which is prone to separation due to a lack of interlocking capabilities. True North backs up their corner technology with a 25-Year "Zero" Air Infiltration Warranty.

Corner Profiles and Posts

Dovetail

Sculptured Dovetail

Saddlenotch

Sculptured Saddlenotch

Proven by design to be the most durable method of construction, the dovetail corner has unique water-shedding capabilities. All angles lead out of the corners so water will never remain at the joint.

The saddlenotch system creates a traditional log cabin appearance, while the incorporation of interlocking logs strengthen the corner. Available in round groove, outside "D" and double "D" logs.

ROUND LOG TIMBER TRUSSES AND PENTA-POST CORNER OPTIONS

True North Log Homes believes that every home should be as unique as it's owner. We offer several custom interior and exterior design features to help define your home. Hand-crafted round log or square timber trusses can be integrated into most any design, to enhance the rustic log home feel.

Large irregular windows or prow-shaped fronts most commonly seen in chalets can be achieved by using True North's penta-post corner system. This revolutionary joinery system allows the interlocking log assembly to conform to irregular angles without compromising the wall integrity.

Ask your True North dealer about these and other designz innovations that will enable you to set your log home apart.

PROBLEM: *Log home corners are NOT held tight, due to obsolete joinery methods.*

The competitor's use of nails, lag screws, or thru-bolts in the corner can actually cause the corner to separate due to log shrinkage. This may permit air into the home.

Nails, lag screws or thru-bolts will create a GAP between the corners over time from shrinkage.

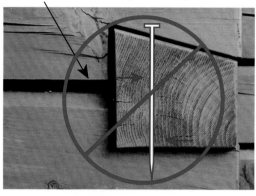

Competitor's corner will shink toward the nail (red arrows)

COMPETITOR'S BANDAGE:

The competitor's customers are expected to fill the gaps around the corners with expensive and labor-intensive caulking or chinking products on a *continuous basis*.

TRUE NORTH'S SOLUTION:

Our KEYLOCK AIR SEAL CORNER system will prevent any air infiltration through the corners. True North homeowners are spared the messy and time consuming task of having to continually caulk or chink the dovetail corners.

True North - 200- Log Homes

The *Patented*
Keylock Air Seal Corner.

EXCLUSIVE KEY-LOCK AIRSEAL CORNER • TRUE NORTH LOG HOMES INC.

TRUE NORTH'S SECRET...

True North uses the naturally occurring shrinkage in the width of the Log to its fullest advantage, making the corner tighter (as shown with green arrows). True North's patented Keylock, when inserted, tightens the Log interfaces together. Over time the Log shrinks towards the Keylock ensuring an airtight seal.

True North's patented Keylock Air Seal Corner® virtually eliminates air infiltration into our log homes.

The absence of nails, lag screws or thru-bolts in our corner system is the major advantage of a True North Log Home. The application of the Keylock Air Seal Corner© ensures no chinking or exterior çaulking will ever be needed on the True North dovetail corner.

LOG LOCK Compression System

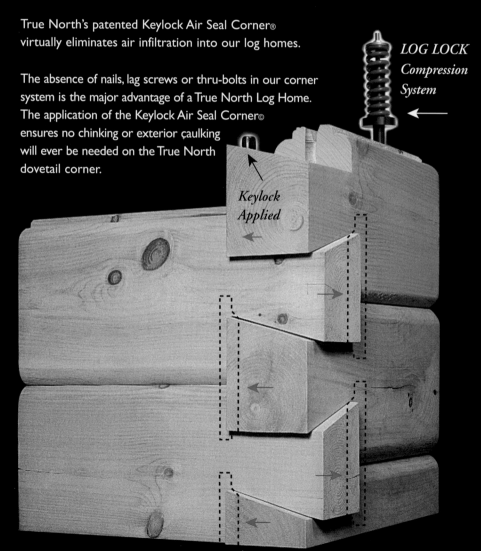

Keylock Applied

Step 1

Log 1 is sawn in half at the factory and is attached to the concrete foundation or subfloor. Two rows of butyl tape and four rows of foam tape are applied to the top of Log 1 in the patented tongue and groove channels.

← *Patented Polypropylene Keylock*

Foam Tape   *Butyl Tape*

Log 1

True North pre-drills a 1-1/8" hole in the centre of the Log as shown in red. A second hole is drilled on the inside face of the Log as shown in blue. When the dovetail is cut, part of the hole, shown in red, is removed.

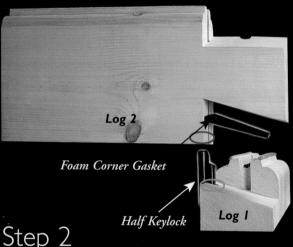

Log 2

Foam Corner Gasket

Half Keylock   *Log 1*

Step 2

The bottom groove of Log 2 is removed at the factory to lay flat on the concrete foundation or subfloor. The patented polypropylene Keylock is cut in half. The top half of the Keylock is driven into the inside face of Log 1, shown in blue. A foam corner gasket is applied to the top of the dovetail on Log 1 to seal the angled surfaces between the dovetails of Log 1 & Log 2. The red hole in Log 2 drops over the half Keylock in Log 1. The inside face of Log 1 is now Keylocked to Log 2, creating an airtight seal.

When the faces of Logs 1 and 2 are brought together, the blue and red holes create a figure 8 shape. A full size Keylock is driven into the inside face of Log 2 (blue hole), which tightens the inside face to the side of Log 1 (green arrow).

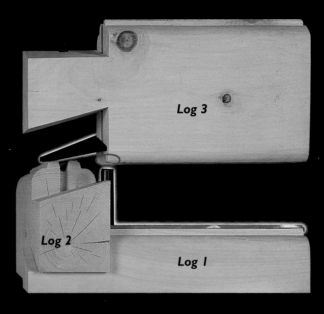

← *Full Size Keylock*   *Pre-drilled LOG LOCK hole* ↓

Log 2

Log 1

Step 4 Another foam corner gasket is applied to the top of the dovetail on Log 2. The red hole in Log 3 is dropped over the Keylock in Log 2.

Log 3

Log 2

Log 1

Step 5 Logs 1, 2 and 3 are now Keylocked together at the interface. The green arrow shows the direction in which Log 2 is tightened. Log 2 will shrink to Logs 1 and 3 creating an even tighter seal over time.

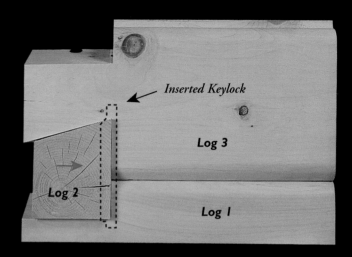

Inserted Keylock

Log 3

Log 2

Log 1

Step 6 On top of Log 2, butyl and foam tapes again set into the tongue and groove channels. Another Keylock is now driven into the inside face of Log 3, which tightens this face to the side of Log 2.

A third corner gasket is applied to the top of the dovetail on Log 3. The red hole in Log 4 is now dropped over the Keylock in Log 3.

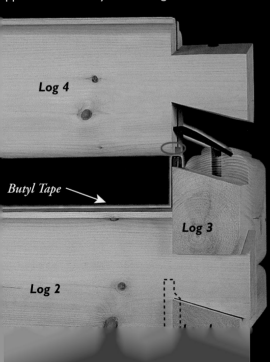

Log 4

Butyl Tape →

Log 3

Log 2

Step 7 Logs 2, 3 and 4 are now Keylocked together at the interfaces. The green arrows show the direction in which Logs 1 and 3 are tightened to Logs 2 and 4 internally by the Keylocks. Log 1 and 3 will shrink to Logs 2 and 4 over time creating a complete airtight seal.

The sequence continues through each course to the top of the Log wall. After the top Log is applied, the LOG LOCK COMPRESSION SYSTEM is installed as shown in the first Keylock corner picture. (far left)

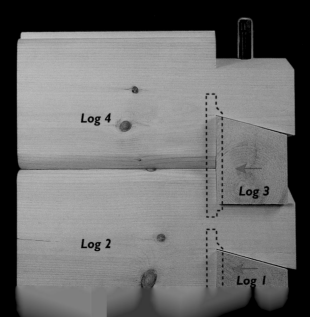

Log 4

Log 3

Log 2

Log 1

What is the advantage to a True North customer?

KEYLOCK MEANS
- **NO AIR INFILTRATION**
- **NO CAULKING OR CHINKING OF DOVETAIL CORNER**
- **25 YEAR "ZERO" AIR INFILTRATION WARRANTY**

PROBLEM:
Overcoming the esthetic and structural issues when the log home design requires angled corner applications. (i.e. turrets, or prow features.)

COMPETITOR'S BANDAGE:

Competitor's typically stick-frame angled corner applications and clad with siding, compromising the structural integrity and esthetic appearance.

Esthetically: Nails used to attach siding can rust and deteriorate.

Structurally: Log walls settle, stick frame walls do not, which may lead to air infiltration. The competitor's customer is required to regularly caulk and/ or chink the transitional joint between the logs walls and the stick-frame walls.

TRUE NORTH'S SOLUTION:

True North's exclusive KEYSPLINE and POST SLIDE technology overcomes all esthetic and structural concerns. This technology provides an airtight seal between a post and a log wall while accommodating all log wall settlement. Our square and penta-posts permit any log wall angles required in log home design.

Installation of KEYSPLINE in Penta-post shown above.

Key Spline*
Post Slide System

* Patent pending

ANOTHER REVOLUTIONARY CONCEPT...

True North's ability to successfully join a Log wall system to a post has become one of its foremost technological achievements. Our Key Spline system significantly expands our Log home design possibilities. We can offer Square Post corners or utilize our exclusive Penta-posts to create any angled log walls desired. Turrets and Prow fronts on your log home are easily accomplished. Log home design esthetic appearance remains intact.

A Bay window wall configuration permits unique room design features i.e. breakfast nooks, hot tub rooms or turrets.

KEYSPLINE ⟶

Post Slide

6 Seals ⟶

KEYSPLINE

KEYSPLINE

KEYSPLINE

KEYSPLINE

Foam Pads

The blue arrows demonstrate the KEYSPLINE pul the Logs tight against the post forming 6 seals. T green arrows demonstrate the Logs sliding dow the Post slide to accommodate Log wall settlemen

(Fig. 1) A "Post Slide" has been factory installed in the channel of the post. Four rows of foam tape are applied vertically on the post from top to bottom.

Log 1 is installed against the post (brown arrow).

Post Slide

Post

Foam Tapes

Log 1

Fig. 1

Half KEYSPLINE

B

2 Foam Tapes

2 Foam Tapes

A

Foam Pad

Log 1

Fig. 2

(Fig. 2) A specially designed foam pad is inserted into the Post Slide in the post and hole of Log 1. Two rows of foam tape are applied to each half of the KEYSPLINE.

The first half KEYSPLINE "A" with a lower tab is inserted into the Post Slide in the post. The second half KEYSPLINE "B" with the upper tab is inserted into the Post Slide above KEYSPLINE "A".

(Fig. 2) The half KEYSPLINES slide together (orange arrows) and interlock to form one complete KEYSPLINE "C".

(Fig. 3) KEYSPLINE "C" and the foam pad are then pushed downward (yellow arrow) along the Post Slide in the post and into the hole of Log 1. The foam pad completely seals between each Keyspline.

Complete KEYSPLINE

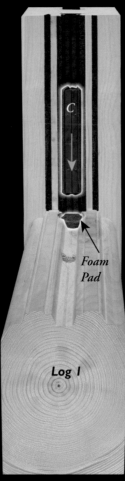

C

Foam Pad

Log 1

Fig. 3

---

10 Inch Spike

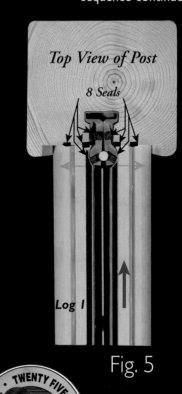

Foam Tape   *Butyl Sealant*

Log 1

Fig. 4

(Fig.4) A 10" spike is then driven into the top end of the KEYSPLINE (white arrow).

(Fig. 5) The spike separates the two halves of the KEYSPLINE in the hole of Log 1 (blue arrows). This action secures and pulls Log 1 tight (purple arrow) forming 8 seals while still permitting the logs to settle against the post.

(Fig. 6) Once the 4 rows of foam tape and 2 rows of butyl tape have been applied to the top of Log 1, Log 2 is then installed (green arrow) and the sequence continues.

Top View of Post

8 Seals

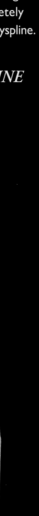

Log 1

Fig. 5

Fig. 6

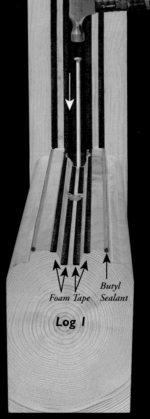

Log 2

Log 1

TWENTY FIVE YEAR • 25 • ZERO AIR INFILTRATION WARRANTY

What is the advantage to a True North customer?

KEYSPLINE MEANS
- **LOG HOME DESIGN "FREEDOM"**
- **AIRTIGHT SQUARE AND ANGLED POST CORNERS**
- **ESTHETIC AND STRUCTURAL ISSUES RESOLVED**
- **LOG HOME ESTHETICS REMAIN INTACT AS STICK-FRAMING IS NOT REQUIRED**

PROBLEM: *Log walls are NOT held tight long term, due to obsolete joinery methods.*

The competitor's use of nails, screws, spring-less or spring only thru-bolts are obsolete fastening devices and may lead to gaps between the logs where air may penetrate the interior of the home.

Competitor's Log wall shown below being caulked.

COMPETITOR'S BANDAGE:

The competitor's customers are expected to fill the gaps between their logs with expensive and labor-intensive caulking and chinking on an *annual basis.*

TRUE NORTH'S SOLUTION:

Our new ratcheting LOG LOCK Compression system virtually eliminates log wall separation. Our True North homeowners are spared the high maintenance cost of caulking and chinking, leaving more time for *living-in* rather than *working-on* their log home. (see right)

New *Log Lock* *
* Patent pending

Compression System

ANOTHER INDUSTRY FIRST...

LOG LOCKS are installed in the centre of the log at approximately six foot intervals and two feet back from the corners. The average size log home will require approximately 40 LOG LOCKS depending on home design, to ensure the log walls remain tight. Competitor's thru-bolts installation time requires 2 days whereas True North's LOG LOCK cuts installation time to 2 hours. A True North customer benefits with major construction labor savings! *See page 206, Question #6 for further details.*

UP TO 2 INCHES OF AIRTIGHT LOG WALL COMPRESSION.

1 inch for a single storey log home and 2 inches for two storey log homes.

Step 1

To begin installation, the first log is turned on its side. The lower ratcheting receiver and a foam pad are inserted into the factory pre-drilled recess in the bottom of the first log (see below). The first log is then turned back over, installed and attached to the foundation. All logs are then stacked to complete the log wall. (see page right)

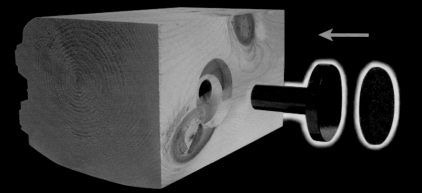

The cutaway view of the LOG LOCK and the lower receiver demonstrates how the internal spring loaded jaws instantly attaches to the threaded rod.

"Our decision to use the new Log Lock system was one of our best. We were able to install all 33 Log Locks in just 2 hours. There was nothing so sweet as the sound and feel of each threaded rod sliding into the base and tightening into place. Well done".

– Marv Nolan, homeowner / self-builder, Ontario

Yellow Zinc Coated Nut

2 Yellow Zinc Coated Washers

2,500 lbs Red Compression Spring (Steel)

Self Tightening Ratcheting LOG LOCK (Steel)

10 ft. Yellow Zinc Coated, Rust Resistant Threaded Rod (Steel)

Lower Ratcheting Receiver (Steel)

Self Adhesive Foam Pad

Step 2

A 10 foot threaded rod is then inserted into the factory pre-drilled chase in the log wall. (see blue arrow to left)

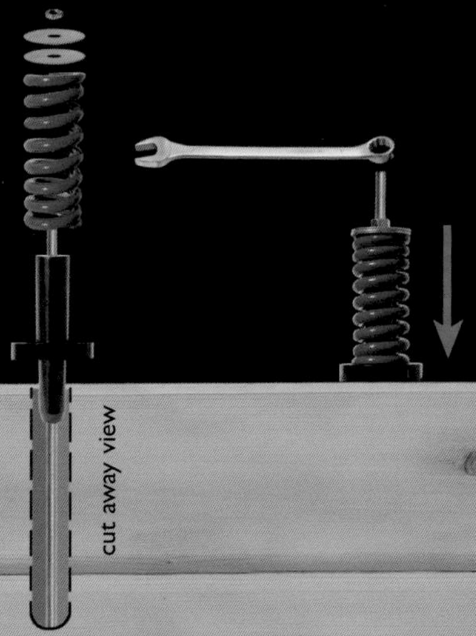

The LOG LOCK automatically continues to self-tighten after initial installation. The competitor's thru-bolt assembly requires their customers to tighten and make adjustments annually.

A True North homeowner is spared this task.

A one inch step in the log wall (shown below) demonstrates the LOG LOCK compression system at work tightening a single storey log home.

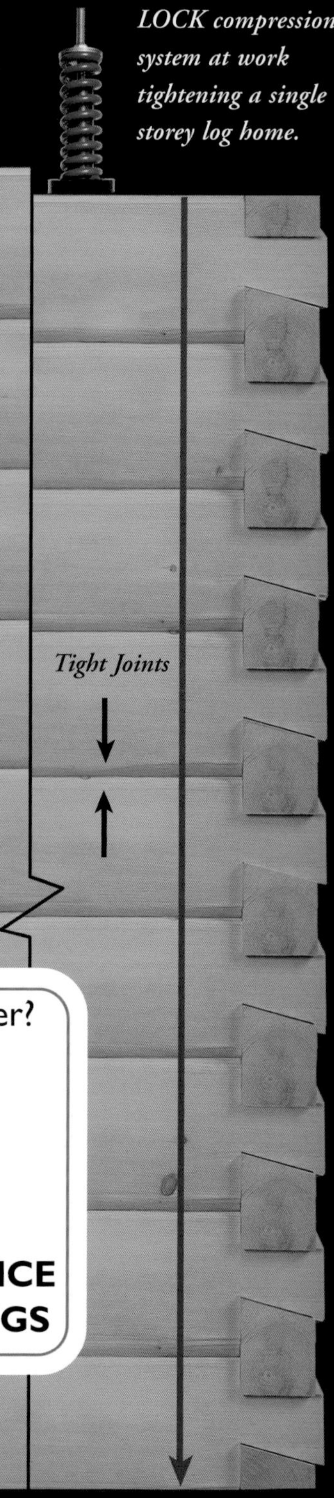

cut away view

Step 3

Once the threaded rod enters the Lower Ratcheting Receiver it is *instantly and permanently* locked into place, no wrenches required here. (see below left)

Step 4

The LOG LOCK, the red compression spring, two washers and a nut are installed. (shown above right) A wrench is used to tighten the nut and washers which compresses the spring. The spring comes into contact with the LOG LOCK forcing it to ratchet down the threaded rod. (demonstrated by green arrow)

Step 5

The LOG LOCK in turn applies pressure to bear on the top log until all of the horizontal joints in the log wall are compressed perfectly tight. (demonstrated by purple arrow)

cut away view

TRUE NORTH'S NEWEST SECRET

The jaws hidden inside the LOG LOCK combined with the 2500 lb. compression spring are designed to permit the LOG LOCK to ONLY go downward one-way on the threaded rod. The LOG LOCK prevents logs from lifting, bowing or separating due to the naturally occurring shrinkage and settlement in log walls.

Tight Joints

TWENTY FIVE YEAR · ZERO AIR INFILTRATION WARRANTY · 25

What is the advantage to a True North customer?

LOG LOCK MEANS
- **NO AIR INFILTRATION**
- **TIGHT JOINTS IN LOG WALLS**
- **NO CAULKING OR CHINKING, EVER!**
- **ELIMINATES ADJUSTMENTS & MAINTENANCE**
- **LIGHTNING FAST INSTALLATION = SAVINGS**

Check out the LOG LOCK movie detailing the installation at www.truenorthloghomes.com/loglock

Just a Moment

Can You Tell Me?

YES we can! Here are the answers to some of the common questions asked by our customers.

WHAT TYPES OF WOOD ARE USED BY TRUE NORTH LOG HOMES?

True North uses winter-cut, slow-growth Northeastern White Pine. This timber is the premium quality of the pine species compared to its lower quality red, yellow and jack pine cousins. Northeastern White Pine grows slowly because of the severity of the climate, producing tight growth rings, resulting in a dimensionally stable log. White pine experiences less shrinkage due to its low sap content and is therefore less likley to warp. True North also uses Western Red Cedar for the client who prefers cedar.

I HAVE HEARD THE TERM "SAPWOOD." COULD YOU EXPLAIN WHAT THIS IS?

Sapwood is the soft outer layer of wood found between the more durable heartwood and the bark. This layer is the unstable section of the log and is most susceptible to shrinkage and insect infestation. True North eliminates this part of the log to help ensure the long-term integrity of the log system and to avoid sap bleeding on the inside log wall faces.

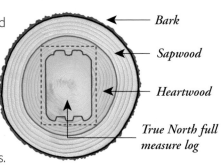

← Bark

← Sapwood

← Heartwood

True North full measure log

IS THERE AN EXTRA CHARGE FOR CUSTOM-DESIGNING MY HOME?

Your personal touch is part of the process and there is never an extra charge to custom design your new True North Log Home.

WHY DO SOME LOG HOME BUILDERS KILN-DRY THEIR LOGS?

For two reasons: 1) Many log home builders kiln-dry because they use standing dead or low-grade wood. Standing dead wood is cut from trees that have been killed by wood borers and other insects. The kiln-drying process attempts to kill these insects prior to using the wood for house construction. This lumber is very inexpensive to purchase. True North uses only live trees with no insect infestation.

2) Log home builders may also kiln-dry in an attempt to reduce the moisture content of logs in an effort to eliminate settlement and shrinkage. The kiln-drying process does not accomplish this because it is impossible to dry out the centre of the log. Usually a kiln dries only the first outside inch of the lumber. Once the log comes out of the kiln, the process is reversed due to the absorption of environmental humidity. Even though some log home builders claim that kiln-drying will totally eliminate settlement and shrinkage, this is simply not true.

WHAT TYPES OF CORNER SYSTEMS ARE AVAILABLE IN THE LOG HOME INDUSTRY?

There are four different systems:

1) Dovetail – This True North system has unique water-shedding capabilities, as all angles lead out of the corner. Interlocking logs make the corner stronger.

2) Saddlenotch – This True North system allows for the traditional log cabin corner appearance by incorporating the interlocking logs to strengthen the corner.

3) Penta-Post Corner – This exclusive True North system allows for post to log interlocking assembly of any non 90⁰ wall angles, ie. for prow living rooms and turrets.

4) Butt and Pass (Not used by True North) – This system is widely used in the industry because it is easier to produce than the other three corner systems. The butt and pass system is prone to separation over time because of its lack of interlocking capabilities. Many log home builders use the butt and pass system because it does not require any sophisticated high-tech equipment to produce, unlike the complex composite angle saw cuts of the dovetail and saddlenotch corners.

YOUR COMPETITORS SEEM EXTREMELY CONCERNED ABOUT YOUR EXCLUSIVE NEW REVOLUTIONARY LOG LOCK COMPRESSION SYSTEM. WHY BUILD SUCH A DEVICE AND WHAT ARE THE ADVANTAGES TO THE HOMEOWNER?

A tree in the forest always grows towards the sun, bending the stem toward the light source. The northwest wind intensifies this hidden bending stress condition forming a "crown" in the tree. When the tree is sawn all of the lumber will be cut straight. As the natural drying process occurs some of the lumber will crown back to the original shape as it was prior to harvesting. A good analogy would be a 2"x4" piece of lumber that is sawn straight and over a short period of time due to the drying process would develop a crown. A larger timber or log takes a longer period of time to dry and as a result may crown after being installed in a log home. This can produce log separation in the log wall that may ultimately lead to possible air infiltration. True North's

Self-adjusting Log Lock applies Downward Force

2,500 lbs Compression Spring

← Log Lock

← Receiver

← Foam Pad

new patent-pending LOG LOCK is the only device of it's kind designed to eliminate log wall separation. The True North homeowner enjoys the added benefits of the LOG LOCK's automatic, "self-adjusting" and "self-tightening" features, which control the natural shrinkage and settlement in the log wall. Future baseboard removal or climbing through the attic space to tighten thru-bolts (as in our competitor's log homes) is never required in a True North Log Home. Lightning fast LOG LOCK installation significantly reduces building time and on-site costs. Complete LOG LOCK installation time is 2 hours compared to a competitor's thru-bolt installation time of 2 days when building an average size log home.

WHAT KINDS OF GASKET MATERIALS ARE USED BY TRUE NORTH LOG HOMES?

True North uses an ultraviolet light (UV) resistant foam gasket material in the tongue and groove and in the corner pads. This material is superior to the white foam gaskets used by other log home builders for three reasons:

1) The True North foam gasket has memory capability – when the foam is collapsed, it will return to its original size; and

2) When compressed 50 percent, our gasket becomes waterproof and will not absorb any moisture from the log; and

3) As ultraviolet light penetrates the log, our gasket will not deteriorate over time.

WHAT IS THE SHRINKAGE RATE OF A TRUE NORTH LOG HOME?

The True North technology, combined with the larger log size used in a True North home, minimizes shrinkage to approx. one inch in an eight foot wall height. This helps to eliminate log movement in your home, ensuring that future structural problems do not occur. The more log courses used in a log home, the more shrinkage will occur. True North is able to minimize shrinkage by using the largest size logs in the industry (12" height), thereby reducing the total number of log courses in the home.

HOW DO LOG HOMES COMPARE TO CONVENTIONAL HOMES WHEN IT COMES TO INSULATION PERFORMANCE?

Log homes do not react to heat the same way as a conventional home. Log homes work on the principle of thermal mass. Thermal mass is the ability of any solid substance that can absorb and hold heat.(i.e. Logs). When the air in a log home is heated, it in turn heats the logs. When the temperature in the room drops, the logs continue to radiate heat back into the room. The larger the log, the more energy it can absorb and the greater the performance. Given the thermal mass capabilities of a True North Log Home, insulation performance would compare to, or surpass, that of an equally-sized conventional home. Our clients consistently tell us how pleasantly surprised they are with their low energy costs.

ONCE I HAVE PURCHASED MY TRUE NORTH LOG HOME, HOW DO I GET IT BUILT?

True North Log Homes and Keylock Project Management work together to create a simple and efficient way for you to build your log home depending on your preferences and budget. The options range from providing your builder with technical assistance, or a complete project management package* which coordinates all aspects of construction for you.

MANY LOG HOME BUILDERS PRE-BUILD THEIR HOMES AND DISASSEMBLE THEM FOR SHIPPING TO THE SITE. DOESN'T THIS GUARANTEE A BETTER FINAL INSTALLATION?

This is an area where True North distinguishes itself from the competition. Every single component of our log system is cut and drilled using computer-aided equipment so that your home can be easily built on-site. The concept of pre-building is generally a result of a competitor using obsolete, low-tech equipment. They must pre-build in order to "proof" their workmanship. This adds considerable cost and creates the possibility of damage while pre-building, deconstructing and final on-site construction.

HOW IS THE ELECTRICAL SYSTEM INSTALLED?

Your local electrical contractor will install all electrical receptacles and switches in your log home. True North can factory drill the vertical holes through the logs for receptacles upon request. Due to electrical requirements in some areas this service may not be available, and therefore must be drilled on-site by the contractor.

HOW DOES A TRUE NORTH LOG HOME COMPARE IN COST TO A HANDCRAFTED LOG HOME OR CONVENTIONAL HOME?

It is a known fact that handcrafted log homes are extremely costly due to high labour costs and time to build them. It is True North's advanced machinery that eliminates man hours and enables us to be extremely competitive with a handcrafted log home and comparative to a well built conventional home.

DO THE OWNERS OF THE COMPANY LIVE IN A TRUE NORTH LOG HOME?

Yes! We are surprised when asked this question. Interestingly enough, we discovered that many owners of other log home companies do not live in their own product.

*Call for availability and construction services in your area.

Keylock Project Management Corporation
P.O. Box 2169, Bracebridge, Ontario Canada P1L 1W1
Phone: (705) 645-6984 Fax: (705) 645-4256
Email: info@keylockpm.com   www.keylockpm.com

True North Log Homes Warranty

Part I

THE TRUE NORTH LOG HOMES, INC. PACKAGE LIMITED WARRANTY:

What we warrant: Subject to the conditions and limitations described herein, True North Log Homes, Inc. ("Company") warrants as follows:

True North warrants that all materials supplied are of accepted standards of quality and grade and are as described in the company's price list and specifications for the type of building purchased and that any defective material will be repaired or replaced, at True North's discretion, without charge upon written notice within 12 months of delivery. No provision is made herein for, checking, cracking, twisting or warping of the wood which would be considered a natural characteristic.

True North warrants that all factory workmanship in the various components, assemblies, and other materials supplied has been completed in a good and workmanlike manner in keeping with accepted standards of manufacture and that any faulty workmanship will be corrected without charge upon written notice within 12 months of delivery.

True North Log Homes, Inc. does not express or imply any warranty on any component part included in its standard package supplied by another manufacturer or supplier. These component parts may be warranted by that manufacturer or supplier.

No warranty covers, and True North Log Homes, Inc. shall have no liability for, any costs or expense of any labour, materials refinishing or painting associated with the installation, removal, or replacement of the defective product or component part, or for any costs, expenses or damage due to accident, fire, act of God, or other cause beyond the control of True North Log Homes, Inc., the building's contractor, or their agents.

Repair, replacement, or refund, as provided under any True North warranty, is the exclusive remedy of the Purchaser and the choice is at the discretion of True North Log Homes Inc.

True North Log Homes, Inc., shall not be liable for any direct or indirect incidental or consequential damages for breach of any express or implied warranty or product.

For replacement, any shortages on the material list must be reported in WRITING to True North Log Homes, Inc., within SEVEN (7) DAYS from delivery of package which is Purchaser's responsibility as time is of the essence.

Part II

THE TRUE NORTH LOG HOMES INC. ZERO AIR INFILTRATION WARRANTY

For a period of twenty-five years, True North warrants to the original purchaser, that the log wall system, including the corners and butt joints, shall not leak air providing that;

a) The log walls were erected according to the plans specifications and construction manual as provided by True North Log Homes, Inc. and all gasket and caulking materials were properly installed and no substitutions were made.

b) The stain product used to protect the logs originally and from time to time is an approved True North Log Homes, Inc. product (ask Dealer for details). The primer coat must be applied at the factory prior to shipping.

c) The purchaser must maintain the exterior of the log building by periodically applying True North stain as not to allow deterioration of the wood or wood joints by the elements of weather, sun or atmospheric conditions.

d) All workmanship was carried out in accordance with generally accepted methods and the foundation remains intact and sound. True North does not design or recommend any particular foundation plan. Local codes govern specifications. Repair, replacement or refund is the exclusive remedy of the purchaser and the choice is at the discretion of True North Log Homes, Inc.

No provision is made herein for air leakage through doors, windows, vents, or other openings. No provision is made for air infiltration through any opening other than the log wall assembly, being that portion under control of spring loaded thru bolts as provided by True North Log Homes Inc.